Plastic Part Technology

Plastic Part Technology

Edward A. Muccio

**The Materials
Information Society**

ASM International® is a Society whose mission is to gather, process and disseminate technical information. ASM fosters the understanding and application of engineered materials and their research, design, reliable manufacture, use and economic and social benefits. This is accomplished via a unique global information-sharing network of interaction among members in forums and meetings, education programs, and through publications and electronic media.

Library of Congress Catalog Card Number: 91-77838
ISBN: 0-87170-432-3
SAN: 204-7586

ASM International®
Materials Park, Ohio 44073-0002

Printed in the United States of America

Acknowledgments

I would like to acknowledge the efforts and support of Dr. Armand Hofer, University of Wisconsin-Stout, Menomie, Wisconsin; Dr. Phillip Reucroft, Professor, Materials Science and Engineering Department, University of Kentucky; Dr. Charles C. Davis, Professor, Mechanical Engineering, General Motors Engineering and Management Institute (GMI), Flint, Michigan; and Mr. Blanding Hensley, Manufacturing Engineering Department, Texas Instruments, Versailles, Kentucky.

Additionally, I would like to thank Mr. Jim Pomeraning of Attwood (a Steelcase subsidiary), Lowell, Michigan, and the staff of the Steelcase Corporate Development Center (CDC) for their technical assistance.

I would also like to thank the students in the Plastics Engineering Technology program at Ferris State University, Big Rapids, Michigan—particularly Glen Henige, Ron Duiz, Marty Paulus, Jeff Smith, Michael Lange, and Frank J. McDonnell. Their interest and thirst for knowledge has been an inspiration. Finally, I would like to thank Professor Henry Tschappat, Director, Plastics Programs, Ferris State University. His vision and support have been invaluable.

Preface

Plastic products are being designed and will continue to be designed by individuals with a wide variety of backgrounds. Some will be familiar with plastics, but most will learn by trial and error. This is not only risky, in terms of product liability, but very expensive.

This book is designed to serve as a "primer" for individuals who design, inspect, manufacture, purchase, and use plastic products. It is written at a level that assumes the reader has little or no experience in working with plastics, and it focuses on the technology versus the engineering aspects of plastic part design.

The unique characteristics of plastics allow them to be used in applications where no other form of material is acceptable, *i.e.*, plastics developed to the point where they are the first materials of choice for new product designs.

Plastic part quality is the premise on which this book is written, with the understanding that to design and manufacture quality plastic parts one must understand how part design, mold design, processing, materials, and the customer relate to one another. All five of these arenas must be represented and comprehended to produce a quality plastic part.

I would like to dedicate this book to Pamela, my love, my life, my best friend, and my wife.

Contents

History and End-Use Markets

Brief History of Plastics

Where did it all begin?

Plastic has been considered an inexpensive alternative to more common materials, such as wood, metal, and glass, since celluloid was first used as an alternative to ivory billiard balls in the late 19th Century.

John Wesley Hyatt, considered by most to be the father of plastics, was applying the unique properties of a plastic to replace ivory, the material of choice for billiard balls. Hyatt's endeavors did earn some praise and money, and by today's standards, he even helped the animal rights cause. His plastic billiard balls, however, were perceived by many as a poor substitute, not equal in value to the original ivory.

Customers, in this case cowboys in the western United States, often found the loud crack of Hyatt's celluloid balls too much like the sound of a pistol. As a result, several gunfights were started simply by a good hard pool break!

Near the turn of the century, photography was coming of age, and cellulose nitrate became one of the first plastics to be the material of choice, not just an inexpensive alternative. All was working well with this plastic application until the development of the motion picture by Thomas Edison, whose creative genius found yet another application to serve mankind. Unfortunately, the early transition from still to moving pictures also tainted the image of plastics. It seems that the cellulose nitrate movie film occasionally jammed and the heat

1868:	Hyatt—Celluloid
1901:	Rohm—Acrylics
1907:	Baekeland—Phenolics
1928:	Carothers—Nylon
1936:	Polyethylene patented
1937:	Polystyrene production
1938:	Nylon first marketed—"Dr. West's" Toothbrush
1939-1950:	Plastics used as an alternative for natural materials (rubber)
1950-1960:	Cheap plastic—"Made in Japan" means poor quality
1957:	Polycarbonate—engineering plastics
1960:	Space race leads to development of advanced plastics
1968:	*The Graduate*
1970-1980's:	Plastics become first choice material—"Made in Japan" means quality

Fig. 1-1 Plastics chronology

of the projector lamp ignited the plastic film, which in turn, set the entire movie theater ablaze! So much for plastic being the material of choice.

After the turn of the century, a series of developments in chemistry led to the creation of several new plastics such as phenolic, acrylics, vinyls, and nylons. A brief chronology is found in Fig. 1-1. Each of these new plastics was developed with no specific applications in mind. Many plastics lingered as mere oddities until a material with one or more of their unique characteristics was needed. World War II was that impetus. Plastics were immediately recruited as (you guessed it) inexpensive alternatives to the more expensive and hard-to-get metals, glass, wood, and silk.

Acrylics were used as bomber blisters, clear canopies, and gun turrets for aircraft. Nylon replaced silk in parachutes, vinyls stood in for rubber in the insulation of electrical wires, and phenolics replaced wood and glass in the electrical market. Plastics proved to be excellent materials when products were designed specifically for them.

After World War II and through the 1950's, just the opposite occurred. The Baby Boom created a market for toys and consumer products that required low-cost materials and low-cost labor. Japan and other Asian-Pacific countries helped satisfy this market with plastic toys and early consumer electronics. The plastics used in these products were intended to be low-cost alternatives with very little attention spent on matching plastic properties to end-use requirements. This resulted in unsatisfied customers and the coining of two phrases, "cheap plastic" and "made in Japan," both of which were synonymous with poor quality.

As the 1960's matured, so did the development of new polymers and plastic compounds. Spurred by the space race and the need for high-tech weapons, families of engineering plastics were developed to meet the rigors of both space and war.

Product designers began to use plastics as the material of choice because of their high strength-to-weight ratios, improved temperature and chemical resistance, and inherent properties of being both thermal and electrical insulators.

The spin-off markets evolved. Plastics usage increased dramatically in the transportation market, achieving two long-sought-for goals not attainable by other materials:

1.   Reduced weight, *i.e.*, better gas mileage
2.   Improved durability

Fig. 1-2 Packaging. P.E.T. bottles. Source: Husky Injection Molding Systems Ltd., Bolton, Ontario, Canada

The consumer electronics business exploded in the mid-1970's, and plastics met the challenge in products such as calculators, audio and video equipment, and telecommunication systems.

Building and construction markets were able to lower costs with items such as rigid PVC plumbing, durable flooring materials, and high thermal insulating materials.

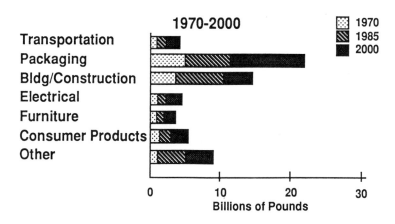

Fig. 1-3 Cumulative plastics growth by market. Source: "Plastics A.D. 2000," Society of the Plastics Industry

Packaging led the way in introducing plastics to the consumer. Plastic milk bottles, soft drink containers, plastic bags, and plastics suitable for the microwave oven are now a part of our lives.

The evolution and development of plastics over the past 100 years can be best illustrated by the change that has taken place in consumers' opinions over the past 30 years. Plastics are now considered to be a first, and often only, choice material, and "made in Japan" now represents quality in manufactured goods.

Plastic End-Use Markets

What are the markets for plastic products?

When this question is asked, most individuals immediately respond "automotive" or "toys." These are probably the most visible end-use markets for plastics, but certainly not the largest.

Packaging

As illustrated in Fig. 1-2 and 1-3, packaging is the single largest end-use market for plastics, and it will probably continue to lead well into the 21st century.

Typical packaging applications include:

- Bottles, films, bags
- Foam packaging material

- Shrink wrap
- Thermoformed blister packaging
- Casings (*e.g.*, compact disc cases)
- Tapes and adhesives

The major future isssue with plastic packaging is disposal. Plastic materials constitute the third largest occupant of landfills (6 to 8 wt% and 16 to 18 vol%) in the United States. Next to paper products, which are first, and yard waste, which is second, plastics are seemingly the most visible. Plastic product designers and engineers are being challenged to anticipate and plan for the disposal of all the products they create. New standards are being developed to code plastics for easy identification and ultimate recycling.

The plastic packaging market from the perspective of materials used is described in Fig. 1-4.

Building and Construction

The second largest end-use market for plastic products is in building and construction. Plastics offer both good thermal and electrical properties, which are needed in today's energy efficient homes and buildings. Plastic piping provides a great deal of design freedom to architects and cost-savings to builders. The barrier materials literally wrap houses in a draft-free blanket, and vinyl exteriors are surpassing all other siding materials because of their color-fastness and durability.

Typical building and construction applications include:

- Plumbing
- Electrical outlets/boxes/wiring
- Sidings, paints, wall coverings
- Insulation and barrier materials
- Bath units
- Laminates (for counter tops)
- Flooring (vinyl and carpeting)
- Adhesives

The major issues associated with plastic applications in the building and construction market are flammability ratings and any potentially harmful by-products that may be generated when plastics are burned.

Plastic materials used in building and construction are described in Fig. 1-5.

Transportation

The third largest end-use market for plastics is transportation. Plastics offer both light weight and high strength-to-weight characteristics, which con-

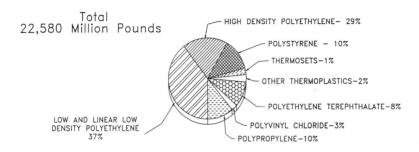

Fig. 1-4 Plastics in packaging by the year 2000. Source: "Plastics A.D. 2000," Society of the Plastics Industry

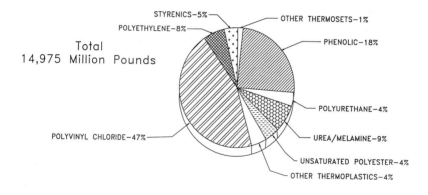

Fig. 1-5 Plastics in building and construction by the year 2000. Source: "Plastics A.D. 2000," Society of the Plastics Industry

tribute to fuel efficiency and higher cargo capacity. The automobile industry has embraced plastics for their durability and functionality, with the average automobile having 250 to 300 pounds of plastics per unit. See Fig. 1-6 for an example of plastics used in transportation.

The aircraft industry is driving the market for composite plastics (*i.e.*, plastic material and reinforcing materials such as glass) to new levels because

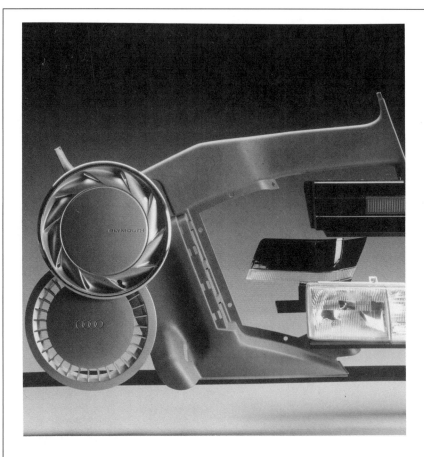

Fig. 1-6 Plastics in automotive markets. Source: Husky Injection Molding Systems, Ltd., Bolton, Ontario, Canada

composite plastics allow aircraft to have unique shapes, smooth exterior surfaces, and considerable weight reduction.

Typical transportation applications include:
- Flexible body panels
- Molded instrument panels
- Lightweight truck cabs
- Plane fuselage and interiors
- Composite frames and springs

- Tires and wheels
- Adhesives

Issues of concern in the packaging and building markets are similar to those of the transportation market. Product disposability and material recycling of automobiles, vehicle safety, durability, and efficiency are among the plastic product design issues that concern end-users.

Electrical and Electronics

Plastic products developed for the electrical/electronic markets (see Fig. 1-7) have historically held the third position in the list of end-use plastic markets; however, the early 1990's have seen transportation advancing and leaving electrical/electronics in the fourth position.

Plastics are dielectrics (insulators), which makes their use in the electronics market a logical one. Early electronic applications for plastics in this arena were primarily as cases or covers. Today plastics are critical to circuit design, electronics packaging, and maximum product functionality. This means the

Fig. 1-7 Plastics in electronic applications. Source: Husky Injection Molding Systems, Ltd., Bolton, Ontario, Canada

product designer can reduce the number of component parts in a complex assembly.

Typical electronic/electrical applications include:

- Wire/cable insulation
- Integrated circuit cases
- Printed circuit boards
- Consumer electronics housings
- Fiber optics
- Connectors, plugs, and sockets

The increase in consumer electronics (computers, VCRs, audio systems, cellular communications) has created a high level of electromagnetic interference (EMI), which is a concern both to health and to reception of electronic signals. The electronics industry is looking toward plastics as a possible solution to prevent the proliferation of EMI radiation. Unfortunately, the good insulating characteristics of plastics tend to conflict with the EMI shielding requirements, *i.e.*, conductivity.

Plastic material suppliers are attempting to formulate and compound plastic resins that act as EMI shields, and electronic assemblers are trying to cope with the problem by coating or plating the inner surfaces of electronic housings to have an EMI shielding effect.

Consumer Products

Consumer products provide plastics with their most visible end-use market (see Fig. 1-8). In this market, most consumers decide whether plastics are an asset (lower cost and improved durability) or a liability (lower quality and lower durability). As mentioned earlier in this chapter, good product design is a balance between material and product design. Those products designed with consideration for the customers' needs are usually successful. Those products designed for short-term monetary gains are often failures.

Plastics offer color, durability, and low maintenance, as well as low cost. These product requirements are forecasted to become more significant over the next 20 years as the population ages and customers want to spend less time on product maintenance and more time on leisure.

Typical consumer product applications include:

- Housewares and small appliances
- Disposable cutlery
- Toys
- Recreational forms of transportation: bicycles, boats, snowmobiles
- Sporting goods

Fig. 1-8 Plastics in consumer products. Source: Husky Injection Molding Systems, Ltd., Bolton, Ontario, Canada

Product safety and durability will be key attributes required of plastic products in the consumer market.

Plastic product designers will be challenged to incorporate several features into products to eliminate parts and reduce assembly and maintenance. Replaceable panels for recreational transportation that simply snap or plug into place will facilitate product repair and life.

Furniture

The furniture market is the sixth largest plastic end-use market and includes many products ranging from low-cost lawn chairs to high-cost office products. Plastic applications in the furniture market include the basic frame or structure, the padding or cushion materials, and the exterior fabrics or upholstery. See Fig. 1-9.

Typical furniture applications include:

- Foam padding/cushions
- Structural components
- Wheels and casters
- Institutional seating
- Laminates and coverings
- Fabrics
- Spring and integral hinged components

Additional markets that are often singled out as major plastics end-use markets include:

- Military products
- Medical
- Industrial
- Adhesives and coatings

End-Use Applications and Plastic Product Design

Understanding the end-use application of the product may seem to be too obvious to be given much thought, but when the plastic product designer overlooks the end-user, product quality is in question.

The end-use examination of a plastic product must consider these factors:

- Temperature ranges (high and low)
- Packaging and shipping
- Chemical exposure—remember milk, soaps, oils, and cleaning materials are chemicals
- Whether the product is to be degreased or cleaned
- Exposure to ultraviolet radiation (outdoor use)
- Exposure to long-term loads
- Exposure to long-term cyclic loads, which cause stress loading
- Method of assembly to other parts
- Disposability
- Contact with humans, animals, or plants
- Agency approval required by Food and Drug Administration (FDA), Underwriters Laboratories (UL), etc.
- Exposure to electricity
- Color

Fig. 1-9 Plastics in furniture. Source: Steelcase, Grand Rapids, MI

The list length is a function of specific product design, but no assumptions of product knowledge should be made. A good product designer will meet and review end-use environments with several individuals prior to starting a design. These individuals may include:

- The customer
- Marketing
- Manufacturing
- Quality assurance
- Operators who manufacture the product
- Mold designers and moldmakers

Since plastic products are unique, one of the best methods for explaining the importance of understanding end-use environments is through some actual cases.

The Case of the Clean Plastic Parts. A complex product was developed for the U.S. Air Force. It consisted of complicated electronics, metal housings, and plastic parts critical to the function of the assembly.

An Air Force general was poised at the end of the product assembly line to view this latest piece of hardware. The last operation in the process (prior to the general's inspection) was a chemical (vat) degreaser.

The unit was soaked in the chemical, and when it was removed, all the polycarbonate parts were gone! Most plastics are sensitive to chemicals and could be affected by exposure.

The Case of the Achilles' Heel. Polysulfone is one of the stronger thermoplastic materials. It is used extensively in aerospace applications; therefore, its selection as a candidate for one of the first low-cost digital watches was considered a bit of an overkill.

Polysulfone, however, is easily stressed when molded. If the stress level in the molded parts is not reduced by a postmolding annealing operation, the material will have a much lower chemical resistance than expected.

Fingernail polish remover, a common household item, is mostly acetone. Ladies who wore digital watch cases molded with polysulfone while they were removing their fingernail polish discovered that their watch cases were literally disintegrating!

When designing a plastic part, the plastic product designer should consider all the possible chemicals (household and industrial) with which the part could come in contact.

The Case of the Smooth Ride. Plastic taillights molded in the Southwest United States were carefully packaged and shipped to one of the "big three" automakers in the Northeast. When the product arrived and was unpacked, it was noted that most of the small assembly tabs on the taillights were broken or cracked.

The failure analysis determined that although the parts were well packaged, the cyclical vibration in the back of the truck caused the tabs to fail. It was also noted that the tabs would not have failed in their actual end-use environment, on the automobile.

Plastic parts subjected to long-term loading and vibration are candidates for failure or permanent deformation. The designer should consider a plastic with adequate fatigue endurance and a design that is robust (unaffected by the environment not directly associated with its intended use).

The next three chapters explain the techniques used to determine end-use property requirements, process selection, and appropriate plastic selection by using the materials matrix.

2

Plastic Materials

A dictionary provides two definitions for plastic:
1. **Plastic:** (adjective) able to be formed
2. **Plastic:** (noun) a synthetic (nonmetallic) material that can be shaped and hardened for use

These definitions do not adequately describe this unique family of materials in a usable manner.

Plastics are more accurately defined as polymers. A polymer is an organic (based on carbon) macromolecule (large in size) that is comprised of several thousand repeating segments (called mers) that are linked together in a chain-like form, as shown in Fig. 2-1.

The number of times a particular segment repeats is referred to as n, the degree of polymerization. As n becomes larger, the polymer molecule becomes longer and the molecular weight of the polymer increases.

The chain-like molecule is often referred to as the carbon chain, as shown in Fig. 2-2. When compared to common materials such as water or oil, the carbon chain molecules that define a plastic are long ($n = 100$ to $n > 1000$).

Why should the product designer understand plastics? As mentioned in Chapter 1, the key to a successful plastic product design is that the designer has considered the product relative to end-use, processing, design, and materials.

Each plastic is unique, and there are thousands of plastics. Understanding how plastics/polymers work will help the plastic product designer make a more informed decision when selecting a plastic for a particular application.

Polymers are:

▼ Organic

▼ Large Molecules

▼ Chain-Like

▼ Made From "Building Block" Molecules

$$
\begin{array}{cc}
H & H \\
| & | \\
C & = & C \\
| & | \\
H & CH_3
\end{array}
\longrightarrow
\left[
\begin{array}{cc}
H & H \\
| & | \\
- C & - & C - \\
| & | \\
H & CH_3
\end{array}
\right]_n
$$

Propylene   Polypropylene

Fig. 2-1 Polymers

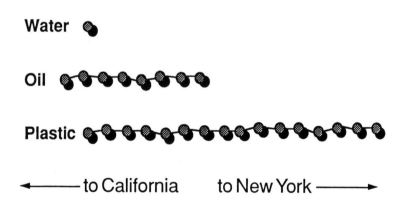

Water

Oil

Plastic

◄─────── to California   to New York ───────►

Fig. 2-2 Long, chain-like plastic molecules

To help understand the effect of the length of plastic molecules, a good example is to think of these long polymer chains as spaghetti cooking in a pot of boiling water. If the average length of each piece of pasta was 2 in., the cook would be hard-pressed to pick up very much on his or her fork. On the other

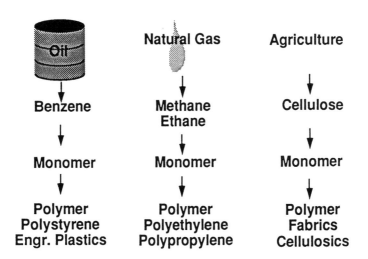

Fig. 2-3 Plastic feedstocks

hand, if the average length of each spaghetti strand was 8 to 12 in., the cook would find that the pasta becomes easily entwined and tangled, allowing a larger amount to be gathered on the fork.

The longer the polymer (plastic) molecules, the more they become entangled. It is this degree of entanglement that helps give the plastic tensile strength, impact resistance, and flow characteristics when processing. This effect is discussed in more detail in Chapter 3.

Feedstock Materials

What is the source of plastics? The feedstock materials for plastics fall into three basic categories (listed in order in Fig. 2-3):

1. Petroleum—usually in the form of a light distillate such as benzene
2. Natural gas—in the form of methane
3. Agricultural materials—could be in the form of wood or cotton (cellulose) or soybean by-products

Petroleum-based feedstock prices and the price of plastic materials should be carefully monitored by large-volume plastic users. See Fig. 2-4. Political factors, environmental concerns, and natural disasters have a major impact on feedstock availability and, therefore, pricing.

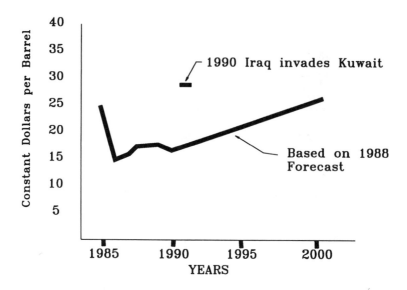

Fig. 2-4 OPEC oil pricing affects the price of plastic

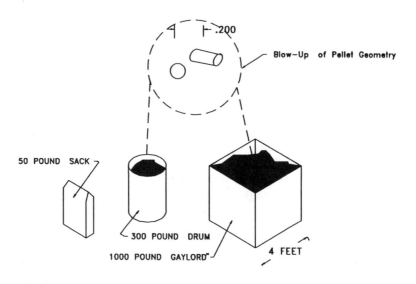

Fig. 2-5 Plastic containers and pellet shapes

The feedstock materials are chemically developed into what is called a monomer, or single unit. The monomer is then reacted with catalyst, heat, and pressure to create the polymer. This process is called polymerization. The polymerization process is usually a batch-type process in which plastic (several thousands of pounds of polymer) is manufactured in large reactors.

The plastic mass has to be granulated and then pelletized to a cylindrical shape approximately 0.060 in. in diameter by 0.180 in. in length. Other plastics, such as polystyrene, can be polymerized directly into a spherical shape. See Fig. 2-5. These shapes allow the plastic processor to conveniently transport and handle the plastics in the various types of processing equipment. Also illustrated in Fig. 2-5 are the three common packaging systems in which plastic pellets are shipped: 50-lb sacks, 300-lb cardboard drums, and 1000-lb gaylords.

Prior to the pelletizing process, the plastic may be compounded with various additives, which are described later in this chapter.

Thermosets and Thermoplastics

Plastic materials are named and classified to the point where many plastic product designers become confused or overwhelmed by the variety of chemical and trade names. To make sense of all the nomenclature, it is best to start with the two major plastic categories: thermosetting and thermoplastic materials. See Fig. 2-6.

Thermoset	Thermoplastic
Set upon heating	Become soft upon heating
Process is irreversible	Process is reversible

Examples:

Epoxy	Polyethylene/Polypropylene
Phenolic	Lexan
Polyurethane, (Foam Rubber)	Rynite (P.E.T.)
Fiberglass	
Tires	

Fig. 2-6 Two major plastic categories

Thermosets

Thermosetting plastics are plastic compounds that set or crosslink upon heating. The crosslinking process actually is the formation of chemical bonds between the long carbon chains. See Fig. 2-7.

The additional chemical bonds of the crosslinked thermosetting plastic allow it to absorb more thermal energy (heat) before the carbon chain is broken. This is the reason thermosetting plastics usually are able to perform at higher temperatures, and it further affords the plastic part designer a material with outstanding chemical and electrical resistance.

This process is irreversible. Once set, the thermosetting plastic cannot revert to its prior stage. An example often used to clarify this irreversible process is the baking of a cake. Ingredients are mixed, and the batter is baked. If the baker is not satisfied with the quality of the cake, there is no way to fix or undo the baking process. It is irreversible. Terms often used to refer to the crosslinking process are:

- Set
- Cure
- Vulcanize
- Kickover

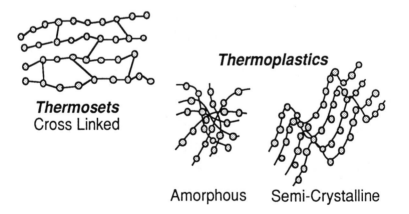

Fig. 2-7 Structure of long plastic molecules

Typical thermoset plastics are listed in Fig. 2-8 with respect to their usage growth.

Thermoplastics

Thermoplastics soften upon heating and harden upon cooling. This process is reversible. An example used to describe thermoplasticity is ice, which hardens upon cooling and can be remolded by heating.

Unlike thermosets, there are no chemical bonds between the long chain molecules (see Fig. 2-7), but the way the thermoplastic molecules position themselves next to each other and the intermolecular forces that hold them together further affects their properties and classification.

Random entanglement of the thermoplastic molecules, much like the long spaghetti on the end of the fork, is called amorphous structure. Amorphous means without a logical order. Amorphous thermoplastics can be clear, have uniform (isotropic) properties in all directions, and have a melting range versus a melting point.

Typical amorphous thermoplastics are:
- Polystyrene
- Acrylics
- Polycarbonate
- Polyvinyl chloride

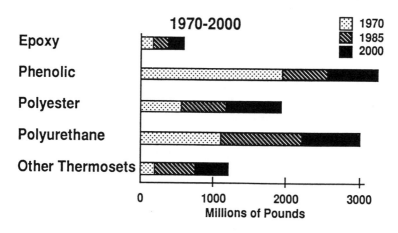

Fig. 2-8 Cumulative domestic thermoset growth. Source: "Plastics A.D. 2000," Society of the Plastics Industry

Molecules that have an order to them are referred to as semicrystalline. Unlike crystal structure in salt or metals, semicrystalline in thermoplastics refers to an occasional order where molecules may line up next to one another. See Fig. 2-7. This semicrystalline thermoplastic is characterized by its opacity, nonuniform (anisotropic) properties, and distinct or narrow melting range.

Typical semicrystalline thermoplastics are:

- Polyethylene
- Polypropylene
- Nylon
- Thermoplastic polyesters

Figure 2-9 highlights a variety of thermoplastic materials by their projected growth.

Forms of Thermoplastics. Thermoplastic materials are found in a wide variety of formats, which include:

- Semicrystalline—often referred to as crystalline
- Amorphous
- Elastomer—materials able to stretch 2 times their original length and fully recover
- Plasticity—the opposite of elasticity, as in an elastomer, meaning the material will tend to remain in its new shape if distorted
- Rigid—materials that are stiff and maintain their shape
- Flexible—materials that are easily folded or distorted
- Ductile—a material that can be stretched or pressed without destroying the basic integrity of the material

With this information, polystyrene (the plastic used to make model airplanes) is described as a rigid, amorphous thermoplastic. Low-density polyethylene (the material used in plastic bags) is a flexible, semicrystalline thermoplastic. Note that a flexible plastic may not necessarily be an elastomer; however, virtually all elastomers are flexible.

Figure 2-10 illustrates the difference in tensile properties between plastics and metal. The stress is the force/area applied in a tensile (pulling) mode, and the strain is the resulting deformation (change in length/original length) of any materials. Stress and strain are discussed in more detail in Chapter 5.

Engineered Thermoplastic Materials

Most of the plastics used today are not pure polymers. The requirements of a specific application and the properties of a plastic may not match. In this

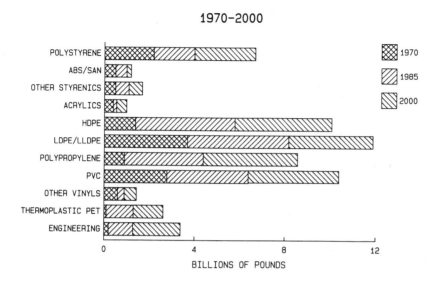

Fig. 2-9 Cumulative domestic thermoplastic growth. Source: "Plastics A.D. 2000," Society of the Plastics Industry

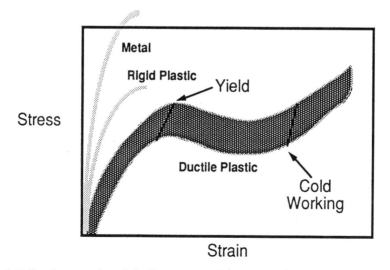

Fig. 2-10 Tensile properties of plastics versus metals

situation, the polymer can be modified or custom engineered to improve specific properties. There are two main techniques for enhancing a plastic: (1) modifying the polymer and (2) creating a plastic compound.

Modifying the Polymer. If the polymer selected is deficient in one or more properties required in the end-use application, it is often possible to create a hybrid plastic by copolymerizing two or more plastics together, thus combining the best properties of each plastic into one material.

An example of a copolymer is polyacrylonitrile butadiene styrene (ABS), which combines three polymers. A stands for the acrylonitrile portion of ABS. Acrylic polymers are known for their clarity, colorability, and brittleness. B stands for the butadiene portion of ABS. Butadiene is a rubber-like material that acts much like a shock absorber in the ABS, thus improving impact resistance. S stands for the styrene portion of ABS. Polystyrene is a clear, brittle, low-cost polymer. When polymerized together, these three different polymers are referred to as a terpolymer and exhibit a phenomenon known as synergism. Synergism means that the result exceeds the sum of the parts. In the case of ABS, the resulting physical properties (low cost, impact resistance, good colorability) are found in the product, not the components.

Another technique for customizing plastics is to physically blend two or more polymers together. There is no chemical bonding in a blend. Often a blend of polymers is referred to as an alloy.

A good example of a polymer blend is that of ABS and polycarbonate. Polycarbonate is known for its high impact resistance and the fact that it is naturally flame retardant. Polycarbonate is also more expensive than ABS.

Plastics customers needed a plastic with better impact resistance and a better flammability rating than ABS, but they could not justify the cost of polycarbonate.

It was determined that ABS and polycarbonate could be made compatible (not all plastics are compatible with each other) and could be physically blended to meet the customer requirements. Figure 2-11 illustrates these two common techniques for engineering polymers.

In addition to copolymerization and blending, polymer engineers can create graft and branched polymers. These graft polymers chemically bond different materials at select points on the carbon chain to customize properties. The branched polymers have a modified carbon chain with smaller chains or branches bristling off the main chain. These branches provide additional strength and rigidity to the polymer.

Additives and Modifiers. Even with all the polymer engineering efforts to customize the characteristics of a polymer to meet specific customer needs,

Plastics Can Be Comprised Of:

Pure Polymer Base
(Polypropylene)

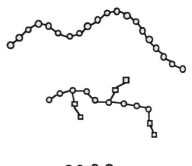

Copolymers
2 or more polymers
chemically joined
(ABS)

Polymer Blends (Alloy)
A physical Mixture of 2
or more polymers
(ABS + Polycarbonate)

Fig. 2-11 Copolymerization and blending

additional property modifications that cannot be met by the polymer itself are still in demand.

Most plastics used today are comprised of the polymer and additive(s). The additive modifies specific properties of the plastic to further characterize the material. These combinations of additives and polymers are referred to as plastic compounds. See Fig. 2-12.

Plastic Compounds

It is unlikely that neat plastic (polymer only, no additives) will have all the desired properties such as:

- Strength
- Density
- Color
- Thermal properties
- Cost

Therefore, a plastic product designer must be familiar with what the additives and modifiers are and how they affect (positively and negatively) the plastic compound and ultimately the plastic product.

Additives and Modifiers

Plastic/Polymers used in most products are PLASTIC COMPOUNDS

Additives and Modifiers

▼ Reinforcements   ▼ Fillers

  • Glass Fibers   • Wood Flour

  • Carbon/Graphite   • Cotton

▼ Colorants   • Clay

▼ Stabilizers/Flame   ▼ Plasticizers
   Retardants
                       ▼ Foaming Agents
▼ Regrind

Fig. 2-12 Plastic compounds

Reinforcements

Reinforcements are used to enhance specific properties. These are usually mechanical properties such as tensile strength or flexural modulus (rigidity). Thermal properties such as deflection temperatures are also augmented with reinforcements. The reinforcement materials are treated with a chemical coupling agent, which helps the reinforcement to remain attached to the plastic matrix.

Major advantages are:

 • Improved strength and rigidity
 • Improved heat resistance

Major disadvantages are:

 • Higher cost
 • Shorter equipment/tooling life
 • Reduced product surface appearance

Glass. The most popular reinforcement material for use with plastics is glass in the form of fibers, which are compounded with the plastics and pelletized for convenient use by plastic molders.

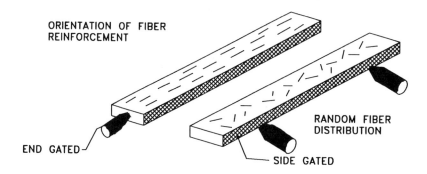

ORIENTATION OF FIBER
REINFORCEMENT

RANDOM FIBER
DISTRIBUTION

END GATED

SIDE GATED

Fig. 2-13 Glass fiber reinforcement of plastic

Because the glass fiber is usually no longer than the plastic pellet (~0.250 in.), the fiber has the opportunity to be molded using the same equipment and molds as plastic without reinforcement. The addition of glass and most other reinforcements will significantly erode both the molding machinery and the mold. Long-term processing costs should be considered when working with heavily reinforced plastics.

Another consideration for the plastic product designer is the fact that the introduction of a fiber into the plastic melt stream may result in fiber orientation (fibers align themselves), which creates anisotropic (uneven) physical properties. See Fig. 2-13.

The two major glass fibers used in plastics today are:

- E-glass: a low-cost fiber with good electric resistance properties
- S-glass: more expensive than E-glass. The S-glass offers improved mechanical strength.

Carbon/Graphite. Used predominantly in advanced plastic materials, carbon/graphite fibers significantly improve the strength and modulus (rigidity) of a plastic.

Mica is a quartz-like mineral that is considered particulate in nature. A particle, unlike a fiber, is unlikely to orient during the molding process and will, therefore, afford the designer isotropic (even) property behavior.

Fillers

Fillers are materials added to plastic specifically to lower cost. They are compounded and pelletized with the plastic materials.

It is possible that a plastic compound contains a filler without the knowledge of the material processor.

Typical filler materials are:

- Wood flour
- Kaolin (clay)
- Cotton and cloth

Although fillers are more commonly used with thermosetting plastics, they are also available for thermoplastic materials.

Major advantages are:

- Lower material cost
- More product per pound of plastic (polymer)
- Improved heat resistance

Major disadvantages are:

- Lower mechanical properties than unfilled plastic (depending on the filler used)
- Higher process variation

Colorants

Colorants are additives used to alter the color of plastic. The science of coloring and color matching is complex and often requires sophisticated equipment to ensure that colorants are both compatible with the plastic and are of the correct type.

The complexity of coloring plastic is increased because each plastic has a different color base. For example, acrylics, polystyrene, and polycarbonates are clear and, therefore, readily colored. Nylon and ABS are naturally brownish in color and are more difficult to color. Thermosetting plastic and reinforced plastic are opaque, limiting the coloring of these materials.

The colorants themselves are usually an organic or inorganic dye or pigment. The amount of colorant added to plastic material is relative to the color of the base plastic, *i.e.*, the darker the base plastic, the more colorant required.

Colorant is mostly precompounded with the plastic, but if justified, colorant can be added to the plastic by the processor. The colorant may be in the form of a powder, liquid, or pellets. A typical colorant is added in the range of 1 to 4% by weight.

Colorants, like all additives, affect other properties; as an example, consider the coloring of plastic either white or black.

White colorant is usually a form of titanium dioxide. When added in sufficient loadings to effect a good white color, the plastic involved could become stiffer and suffer from a decrease in flexibility.

Black colorant is usually a form of carbon black. When added to many plastics, the rigidity of the material is increased.

Although these second-order effects may be desirable, they must be understood. A product design with a natural (uncolored) nylon plastic may perform differently than the same product manufactured with a white nylon material.

Major advantages are:

- Wide range of available colors
- Coloring is throughout the material

Major disadvantages are:

- Higher cost
- Possible negative effect on other properties
- Difficult to match colors
- Batch-to-batch color variations
- Colors change when exposed to heat and sunlight

Flame Retardants and Stabilizers

Plastic materials burn. The control that most designers want in their selected plastic is to be able to slow the burning rate sufficiently to meet agency and consumer requirements. Flame retardants are added to plastics to slow the rate of burning and/or to create a plastic that will not be able to support a flame.

Flame retardants fall into two main categories:

1. Compounds that when heated will generate a gas that starves a flame by removing the available oxygen
2. Other plastics that are more flame retardant and are blended with the selected plastic

The issues associated with plastic flammability are controversial, and careful consideration by the plastic product designer must be made to understand the value of adding a flame retardant to a plastic versus selecting a more naturally flame retardant material.

Flammability ratings for plastics are somewhat subjective and confusing. They are a function of wall thickness; for example, a plastic with a 94 VO rating with a wall thickness of 0.125 in. may have a different rating (more flammable) with a wall thickness of 0.0625 in.

Major advantages are:

- Reduced flammability
- Improved heat resistance

Major disadvantages are:

- Higher cost
- Possible processing problems
- Reduced mechanical properties

Stabilizers

Stabilizers are additives that help to control or enhance specific properties. As with all additives, there may be negative aspects to their addition in a plastic system.

Thermal stabilizers are used to improve the long-term stability of plastics when exposed to heat. Many plastic parts may distort when they are within 20 to 40 °F below the end-use temperature. The thermal stabilizer will afford the plastic the widened temperature range required to meet an application.

Thermal stabilizers are often used in heat-sensitive plastics such as polyvinyl chloride (PVC).

Plasticizers are chemicals added to plastics (usually polyvinyl chloride) to make them flexible. Like many additives, plasticizers vary in their compatibility with the plastic compound. As a result, the plasticizer may become extracted from the plastic over time. A good example of this phenomenon is automobile seats. When purchasing a new car, you immediately become aware of the new car smell. This aroma is actually a combination of odors that include carpeting, adhesive, paints, solvents, and plasticizers used to keep the vinyl upholstery supple. (If you have leather seats, don't worry. You will still have vinyl in the padded dash!) Over time and variations in temperature, and through sliding in and out of the car, the plasticizer is gradually removed from the upholstery. The milky mist that lingers on the inside of the windshield of a new car on a hot summer day is also plasticizer.

After enough plasticizer is extracted from the vinyl, the flexibility of the material decreases, and the seats and padded dash blister and crack.

A new market has developed to combat this problem, *i.e.*, spray-on protectants. These spray-on products are actually plasticizers that coat the surface of vinyl preventing any further plasticizer, from within the vinyl, from being extracted.

Ultraviolet (U/V) Light Stabilizers. Many thermoplastics have a tendency to fade in color or physically degrade when exposed to sunlight. The U/V stabilizer provides the plastic with the needed U/V resistance to be used in exterior applications. A good example of plastic that requires U/V stabilization is polycarbonate. This strong thermoplastic could not compete against other plastic materials in applications such as auto taillight lenses if not for U/V stabilization.

Some colorants, such as carbon black, provide U/V stability as a secondary benefit.

Antistatic Agents. One of the advantages of plastics is their inherent dielectric abilities. The fact that most plastics do not conduct electricity becomes a problem when static electricity needs to be dissipated.

Electric charges that accumulate on the surface of a plastic will remain there until neutralized.

Antistatic agents fall into three major categories, as shown in Fig. 2-14: internal, external, and ion discharge.

Internal. These are chemicals that are compounded in the plastic and will migrate or bloom to the plastic surface due to their incompatibility with the plastic. Upon reaching the surface of the plastic, the surface resistivity of the plastic is decreased; *i.e.*, the surface becomes more conductive. This change in the electrical characteristics of the surface is enough to dissipate the static charge. The internal antistatic agent has a finite life, and the effect gradually disappears.

Internal antistatic agents have proven helpful in the recording industry where static charge on the surface of the plastic product (phonograph records and compact discs) means an increase in the attraction of dirt and dust.

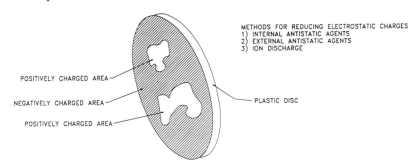

Fig. 2-14 Antistatic agents in plastic

External. These antistatic agents are applied to the surface of a plastic part after it has been manufactured. The principle of decreasing surface resistivity is the same as that of the internal antistatic agent.

External antistatic agents are more effective than internal antistatic agents; however, they are also more short-lived.

External antistatic agents have created a niche market with the development of the anticling dryer sheets. Polymer fabric surface conductivity is temporarily increased, and the clothes lose their static charge.

Ion Discharge Antistatic Systems. The electronics and packaging industry had a need for short-term static charge dissipation. The use of ion sources, generated electrically or via low-level radiation, has answered this need.

A plastic product is exposed to a slightly ionic atmosphere, such as an air stream, that is charged oppositely to that of the surface electrons that cause static electricity. The static charge on the surface of the plastic is temporarily neutralized.

This process is particularly useful in the dissipation of static charges on plastic parts with complex shapes.

Biocides. Many plastics have a propensity to attract undesirable life-forms, such as fungus and bacteria. Plastics have also been known to be a food source for undesirable creatures such as rodents.

Underground conduit and plumbing product manufacturers, in particular, have found that biocides added to the plastic may provide adequate resistance and protection from these pests.

Foaming Agents. Cellular plastics (foamed plastic) have been of particular value as thermal insulation products servicing building and construction as well as packaging markets.

All plastics can be foamed by the introduction of an additive or filler. There are three main foaming techniques: internal blowing agents, external systems, and microballoons or microspheres.

Internal blowing agents are compounds that are added to the plastic and decompose within a specified temperature range during molding. The decomposition of the internal blowing agent results in the evolution of a gas, usually nitrogen, that will form a cellular structure when allowed to expand in the plastic melt.

External systems are usually gases, steam or nitrogen, that are physically introduced into the plastic melt to provide the cellular structure.

Microballoons or microspheres are small hollow spheres (<0.010 in. in diameter) that are mixed with the plastic (usually thermosetting plastic) and are the cell structure for what is called a syntactic foam.

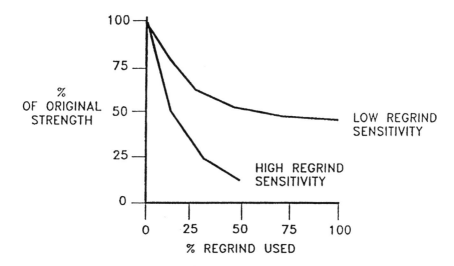

Fig. 2-15 Regrind as an additive

Regrind. This is thermoplastic material that has been granulated and reintroduced into the process, usually by mixing with "virgin" plastic. The introduction of regrind allows a plastic processor to get the maximum material usage; however, the regrind is not exactly the same as the virgin material and may negatively affect the process. Regrind, when compared to virgin plastic, has:

- Been exposed to a longer heat history
- A different shape; therefore, it processes differently
- A reduction in physical properties (see Fig. 2-15)
- An altered color or has been contaminated

The plastic product designer should specify the maximum regrind allowed, for a particular part, directly on the print. This includes specifying "No regrind allowed" if that is what is required.

Plastic part designers should consider the issue of regrind, not only in the part design, but in the process and tooling as well. Many times plastic parts can be molded with little or no nonproduct material generated; thus no regrind is considered.

More information on plastic materials is discussed in Chapter 5, which explains how to differentiate and select a plastic material for a specific application.

3

Processing of Plastics

Plastics processing is the conversion of a plastic compound into a plastic part.

As simple as it may sound, the plastic process is quite complex and may actually reduce the properties of the plastic compound to the point where it no longer satisfies the customer's requirements. Understanding how to process plastic materials properly is constantly being studied. Plastic part designers and customers must understand the basic plastic processes used in the manufacturing of their product. This awareness must include both the quality impact and the cost impact a process may have on their product.

Although there are a multitude of plastics processing techniques, many of them are variations of what are referred to as core processes. These core or primary processes are:

- Compression molding
- Transfer molding
- Extrusion
- Blow molding
- Injection molding
- Thermoforming
- Composite processing

For the sake of comparison, each process is reviewed relative to concept (including typical plastics used, history, and overview), typical parts produced, tooling, cost, and quality.

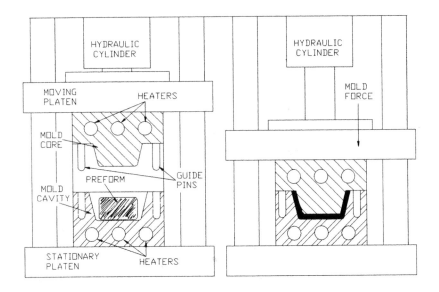

Fig. 3-1 Compression molding

Compression Molding

Concept

Compression molding is the oldest plastic processing technique. The process has been used for thousands of years with many different materials, including the most basic of all materials—earth and water—used to make bricks.

The basic process involves a two-piece mold held vertically (see Fig. 3-1 and 3-2) in a mold press. The lower half of the mold is the female half (called a cavity). The material to be molded (mud, concrete, plastic, or glass) is loaded into the cavity. The upper portion of the mold is a male design, also called the core, force, or plunger, that will apply pressure to the material being held in the lower mold half and compress the material. During compression molding of plastics, heat is required in addition to pressure in order to soften and act as a cure for thermosets or a melt flow for thermoplastics.

The majority of compression molding today is accomplished on sophisticated molding equipment (see Fig. 3-3) that accurately controls the quantity of the material loaded into the cavity, as well as the times, temperatures, and heat applied in the process.

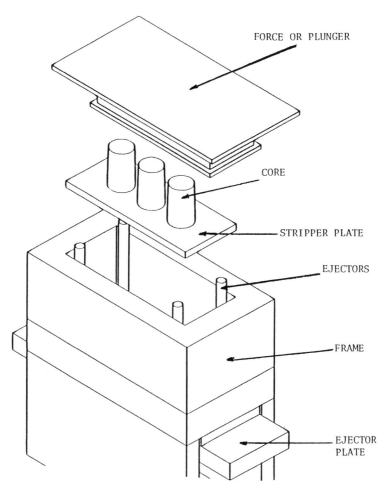

FORCE OR PLUNGER

CORE

STRIPPER PLATE

EJECTORS

FRAME

EJECTOR
PLATE

Fig. 3-2 Compression mold with stripper insert

Compression molding materials are mostly thermosetting plastics and rubber. Typical compression molding materials include:

- Phenolic
- Epoxy
- Melamine formaldehyde
- Urea formaldehyde
- Natural and synthetic rubbers

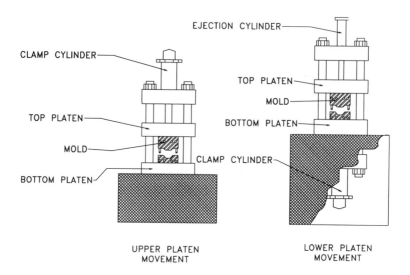

Fig. 3-3 Compression mold presses

The compression molding process is one of the few plastic processes that does not require the plastic to flow or travel any significant distance to fill the mold. This lack of motion results in very low molding or shear stress being introduced to the part during the molding process. The low level of stress means that compression-molded parts tend to hold their shape better than those made by other processes. Round thermosetting plastic parts, in particular, are excellent candidates to be compression molded.

The final curing of the part is controlled by a combination of three variables: time, temperature, and pressure. Each variable in the process must meet the material and part requirements to produce a quality part.

Because there is very little plastic flow required during the compression molding process, the plastic can have a high viscosity (thick, with a high resistance to flow). This allows the compression-molded part to have a thicker wall section if required by the part designer.

The vertical molding orientation of most compression molds is attractive when molding inserts, such as metallic threads or plates, directly into the plastic part or when incorporating other materials or reinforcements (glass mat) into the plastic during the molding process.

Typical Plastic Parts

Typical compression-molded parts include:

- Automotive distributor caps (phenolic)
- Electrical switch plates
- 110-volt electrical sockets (urea)
- Dishware (melamine)
- Rubber tires

At one time, compression molding was considered a slow process, mainly because most older compression molds and machines were designed to have the plastic material manually loaded, and the molded parts were manually removed. As with any process, today's demands for minimum part-to-part variation have dictated that the role of the machine operator be reduced or eliminated. Today's compression machines are configured with automatic plastic material preheating, precise automatic material loading, and auto ejection of the molded part. Regardless of the degree of sophistication of the equipment, the key steps in the compression process remain basically the same:

1. Mold opens.
2. Material is loaded into the mold cavity.
3. Mold closes, compressing the plastic.
4. Mold may be opened slightly during the cycle and quickly closed to allow the process to breathe and vent air and gases.
5. After the plastic has had time to set, the mold opens.
6. The molded part is ejected.

Note some key points about these steps: (A) The material that is loaded into the cavity may take several forms including powder, granular, or premeasured pills. (B) To facilitate the compression process, it is often desirable to preheat the plastic material. This preheating will allow easier material flow and faster molding cycles. The preheating can be accomplished by several techniques including: convection oven, infrared heat lamps, and microwave or dielectric frequency heating, which is the most common.

Tooling

The molds employed by the compression molding process are relatively simple when compared to the molds for other plastic processes such as injection molding.

The compression mold is designed to intentionally flash. Flash is a thin layer of plastic at the parting line. The flash is excess plastic material, which is

POSITIVE MOLD   FLASH MOLD

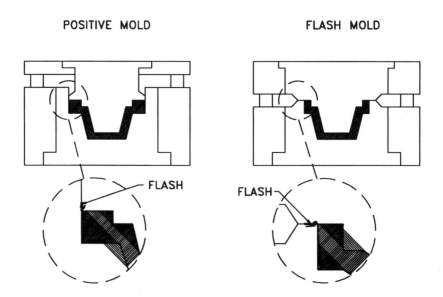

Fig. 3-4 Types of compression molds

an undesirable feature of this process. The reason for the flash is that the amount of plastic material loaded into the mold must be sufficient to make the plastic part; however, there must be extra plastic material to ensure that the molded plastic part is completely filled. There are several different compression mold designs to accommodate this flash, as illustrated in Fig. 3-4.

The compression molds are designed and built to withstand the rigors of high-pressure compressive forces that can easily exceed 200 tons. The molds must withstand the high mold temperatures (350 to 400 °F) required to process and cure most thermosetting plastics. In addition, the compression molds must resist the highly abrasive nature of the plastic material, including glass and mineral reinforcements. Most compression molds are electroplated with hard chrome ~0.001 in. thick to provide extra abrasion resistance.

The tool steel used in compression molds must be tough. Unlike other molding processes, the compression mold core is directly responsible for compressing and working the plastic material. A good quality steel mold such as S-7 offers the designer the shock resistance, toughness, and hardness demanded of the compression molding process.

The mold life expectancy of a compression mold is 500,000 cycles before a major mold refurbishment is required.

Cost

The cost of a compression-molded part, as with all molded parts, depends on the amount of plastic required per part, the cycle time, the intricacy of the tooling, and the amount of labor involved in both the molding and the finishing operations of the part.

Material. Thermosetting plastics vary in cost from $0.50 to $3.00/pound. The density may vary between 1.4 and 1.9, depending on how the specific plastic is reinforced and/or filled. Another material factor concerning com-pression-molded parts is process efficiency, or how many molded parts are wasted over the course of a production run.

Cycle Time. Compression molding of thermosetting plastic is a slow process. With cycle times varying from 40 to 300 seconds, it is easy to under-stand why the process must have a high yield. The main opportunity to reduce the molding cycles is provided by preheating the plastic. Preheating eliminates the need for 100% of the thermal energy to come from the mold. Dielectric heating of thermoset preforms may reduce the overall processing cycle time 50 to 75%.

Other cycle time reduction opportunities are in the areas of automation and operator labor reduction. This is just as important after molding as during molding. Since compression-molded parts have flash, that flash has to be removed. The amount of labor associated with this finishing operation can significantly affect product cost.

The most common deflashing techniques include:

- Hand deflashing
- Tumbling
- Tumbling, with media impacting the parts (see Chapter 9)

When thermosets are molded by the compression process, it may be pos-sible to reduce the cycle time by removing the molded parts from the mold early, as the parts are formed. It must be understood that the thermosetting plastic may not be completely cured, or crosslinked, when the part is removed. Plastic parts molded in this fashion should be allowed to pass through a postmolding curing oven (temperature ~300 °F) for 2 to 3 hours to complete the cure. The postmolding curing process is much lower in cost and higher in throughput than the practice of curing parts while they are in the mold, but there may be quality problems associated with part shrinkage and warpage during oven postcure as well as low density and lower overall strength.

Quality

Specific areas of quality concern when utilizing the compression molding process include: underfill, voids, blisters, and tooling marks.

Underfill. The precision of controlling the amount of material in the cavity can easily be insufficient.

Voids. In addition to the fact that the basic molding process tends to trap air in a poorly vented mold, it should be remembered that thermosetting plastics are also undergoing a chemical reaction. During this chemical reaction, molding gases can be trapped under the surface and result in a void or a hole that can weaken the part.

Blister. Caused by the same factors as voids, blisters are simply voids that have come to the surface.

Tooling Marks. The nature of the compression molding process lends itself to mold damage, especially in the weaker areas of the mold such as ejector pins. The compression-molded part may be pressed into the cavity with enough force to distort or break the ejector pins used to push the plastic part out of the cavity may distort or break. If left unnoticed, this damaged pin will soon damage other portions of the mold. The mold surface condition, of course, will be reflected on the plastic part as an unwanted scar.

Flash

Since flash is a by-product of the compression molding process, removal of the flash is critical. The flash will occur where two metal surfaces come together, such as at the parting line, at the intersection of mold inserts, at the knock out pin sites, at vents, or, of course, at points where flash is designed to occur.

Future

The future of compression molding is heading toward a much more precise process that eliminates the flash aspect of the current process and incorporates more in-line automation techniques to heat material, load material, and extract parts. Additionally, the integration of compression molding techniques with other processes, such as injection molding, will allow more sophisticated parts to be produced that have high heat resistance and rigidity.

Transfer Molding

Concept

Transfer molding has several similarities to compression molding. In fact, many of the compression molding presses can also be utilized as transfer molding machines with little or no modification.

The following features of transfer molding differentiate it from compression molding are:

- Material is loaded into a shooting or transfer pot.
- Material is forced into the transfer mold via a transfer ram or plunger.
- The transfer mold may be a direct shot or be designed with runners and gates to transfer material from the shooting pot to the cavity.
- The transfer process has faster cycles than compression processes.
- There is more waste—runners, gates, culls—in transfer molding.
- Transfer molding lends itself to overmolding or encapsulating other materials or parts.

Figure 3-5 illustrates the basic steps in transfer molding.

Many plastics experts consider transfer molding to be the direct predecessor to injection molding as well as being a process that helped plastic products

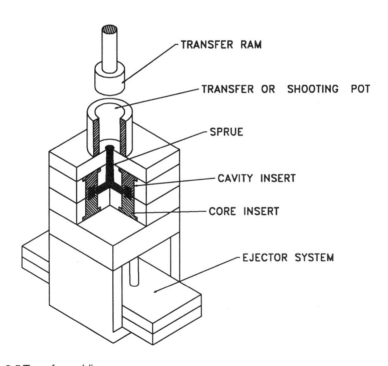

TRANSFER RAM

TRANSFER OR SHOOTING POT

SPRUE

CAVITY INSERT

CORE INSERT

EJECTOR SYSTEM

Fig. 3-5 Transfer molding

enter the high-volume consumer marketplace in the early part of the 20th century.

Transfer molding materials are mostly thermosetting plastics and rubber. The family of materials that use compression molding processes can be adapted to the transfer molding process. The plastic may have to be modified slightly to provide easier or improved flow characteristics that allow it to move through the narrow runners and gates.

The operation steps in the transfer molding process are:

1. Plastic material is loaded into the shooting pot. The amount of material loaded is estimated and then refined with subsequent moldings. The actual quantity of plastic is the sum of the volume of the mold cavities plus runners plus cull. Once accurately determined, the loading of the shooting (transfer) pot may be facilitated by using the preforms, which are prepressed pills of plastic. The preform can then be preheated either in an external microwave (dielectric) heater or in a heated shooting pot. The preform and the preheating allow for faster molding cycles, better plastic flow, and more precise and efficient molding.
2. The mold closes under pressure, and the transfer ram forces the heated plastics from the shooting pot into the mold.
3. The ram remains, holding the plastic under pressure until the plastic begins to cure or solidify.
4. The ram retracts, with the mold still closed, and the cull (cure material that remains in the shooting pot) is released from the ram. The plastics curing cycle is allowed to complete.
5. The mold opens and the part(s) and runner(s) eject.
6. The cycle repeats.

Transfer molding cycles range from 30 to 150 seconds when using preheated preforms.

Typical Plastic Parts

Some examples of transfer-molded parts include:

*   Integrated circuits (IC) or chips
*   Thermoset parts that require metal inserts
*   110-volt electrical outlets
*   Electrical switch gear and circuit breakers
*   Handles for cooking utensils

The transfer molding process requires the plastic molding material to be subjected to high pressures while it is being forced through the narrow runners and the restrictive gate areas. The pressure and material movement impart a significant amount of shear stress on the plastic. The higher stress levels experienced in transfer molding, versus compression molding, will make the molded part susceptible to higher shrinkage, warpage, and possible dimensional control problems.

Tooling

The molds associated with transfer molding are more complicated than those used in compression molding. The runner and gate system in the transfer mold must be designed and built to be balanced, *i.e.*, so that it will allow the cavities to fill with plastic at the same rate. The gates must allow material into the cavities at a uniform rate and "freeze off" to prevent any reduction in cavity pressure.

Transfer molds are made of tool steel that can be hardened to 56 to 60 HRC to reduce wear caused by the flow of abrasive molding compounds under high pressure. Additionally, many transfer molds are often electroplated with chrome to improve surface hardness and provide a smooth surface.

Transfer molds often are designed with many inserts or interlocking components. This is to allow specific high-wear areas to be replaced without replacing the entire cavity. A good example is the gate insert and runner bars. Both the gate and runner in a transfer mold are prone to early wear. By designing these areas as replaceable inserts, they can be tooled with special abrasion-resistant metals and replaced or refurbished quickly and with significantly less expense than if they were integral components of the mold.

Cost

Plastic parts molded using the transfer process are usually less expensive than similar compression-molded plastic parts. This is mainly due to the increase in productivity associated with using multiple-cavity molds in the transfer process and the automation capabilities afforded by the nature of the process.

Note that the material costs for a transfer-molded part are higher than those for a compression part because of the nonproductive material or waste associated with transfer molding. Culls, sprues, runners, and gates are nonrecoverable waste that does not exist in compression molding and must be considered in the material cost analysis.

Quality

The transfer-molded part offers some advantages and disadvantages when comparing part quality relative to compression molding.

Advantages include:

- Easier-to-mold thinner wall sections
- More complicated shapes possible
- Less part flash
- Ease of overmolding or insert molding

Disadvantages include:

- Higher internal stress
- Thicker wall sections are difficult to mold
- Gate scar must be present

Future

Transfer molding will continue to be a viable process for thermosetting plastics and rubber materials, especially in the niche market of insert molding for the electric/electronics industry. However, the transfer molding markets are threatened by advances in thermoset injection molding, which could take over virtually all applications of transfer processing.

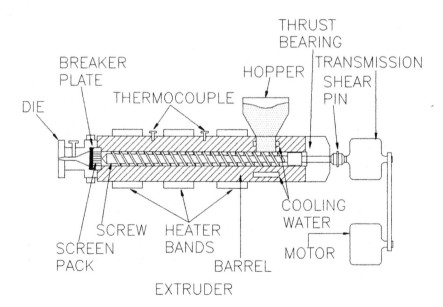

Fig. 3-6 Component of a single-screw extruder

Extrusion

Extrusion is the largest (highest volume) process used to convert plastic material into plastic product.

The process can be described simply by saying that the extruder melts thermoplastic materials, augers or pumps plastic, and forces the plastic melt through a die (see Fig. 3-6).

Extrusion was adapted to the plastics industry from the metals industry where, for hundreds of years, metal has been melted and forced through dies to manufacture pipes for the plumbing industry. Food processing could be called a precursor to plastics extrusion when spaghetti and pasta, and hamburger manufacturing are considered!

Extrusion in the plastics industry is classified into major categories:

- Film—flat layers of plastic under 0.010 in. thick
- Sheet—flat layers of plastic over 0.010 in. thick
- Profile—tubes, rods, and detail shapes

The plastics that use the extrusion process are mainly thermoplastics, but the rubber industry uses extruders for thermosetting rubber materials. Some of the more common plastics that are extruded include:

- Polyethylene
- Polyvinyl chloride (PVC)
- Polystyrene
- ABS

Extruders are also used by the plastic industry as basic compounders. Plastic material and additives are blended together and fed through an extruder for mixing. The extrusion die, in this case, is a series of holes ~0.125 in. in diameter. This type of die will produce a series of plastic rods that will be chopped into short (0.250 to 0.500 in.) lengths to facilitate material handling and be used in other processes, such as injection molding, blow molding, and extrusion of product.

The extrusion process also plays a role in other processes. In order to plasticize or melt the plastic in blow molding and injection molding equipment, a variation of the extruder is adapted for these processes. The use of extruders for plasticization will be discussed later in this chapter.

Typical Plastic Products

The extruded plastic product has had a major impact on our lives—from the simplicity of a plastic bag to package our food to the durability of vinyl siding.

Categorizing the extruded product aids in understanding typical applications. See Fig. 3-7.

Extruded film includes:

- Polyethylene bags and barrier material
- Plastic shrink wrap
- Mylar for audio and video tape
- Carrier materials for printer ink ribbons
- Co-extruded films—multilayered films that can be made using several different plastics

Extruded sheet includes:

- Sheet stock for thermoforming
- Clear panels for signs and construction
- Flooring materials
- Extruded foam sheeting

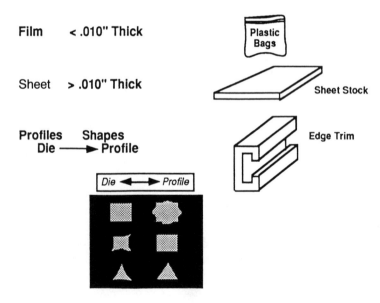

Fig. 3-7 Extruded products

Extruded profiles include:

- Vinyl siding and gutters
- Rubber and elastomeric gaskets for doors and windows
- Pipe, hose, and tubing
- Co-extruded profiles that are made of several different plastics
- Wire and cable insulation that extrudes plastic over metal wire

In addition to the extrusion of plastic as a solid or uniform material, plastic foam can also be extruded. Before the plastic exits the extrusion die, a gas (usually nitrogen) is introduced into the plastic melt stream. This is accomplished either by the chemical decomposition of an additive called a blowing agent or by the direct introduction of gas. The result is a cellular structure material in the form of a sheet or profile. The cellular structure affords the plastic product a much improved thermal insulation (versus the solid plastic), which makes applications that demand a high degree of thermal insulation possible. Examples of extruded foam products include:

- Insulating panels for building and construction
- Fast food packaging—extruded foam sheet that is later thermoformed
- Noise reduction paneling for construction and the auto industry
- Protective packaging sheet—polyethylene and polystyrene

Tooling

Tooling for the extrusion industry is mainly in the form of extrusion dies. These dies are designed to shape the cooling plastic melt into a specific form or shape. In the past, the dies for profiles, for example, were designed and built by trial and error, which was expensive. Today, extrusion die makers employ computer analysis of the die design before it is built and use the latest technology, such as wire EDM, during the die construction.

One of the unique phenomenan associated with extrusion dies is die swell, in which the extrudate (plastic extrusion) expands as it exits the die. The extrudate does not reflect the shape or profile of the die (see Fig. 3-7). The die design must compensate for die swell in order to produce a usable product.

Today's tooling technology, which includes computer aided design (CAD), computer aided machining (CAM), and electrical discharge machining (EDM), facilitates die construction and allows complicated profile dies to be designed and built that would have been impossible 20 years ago. Figure 3-8 illustrates the basic concepts of wire EDM, and Fig. 3-9 shows several dies produced using wire EDM.

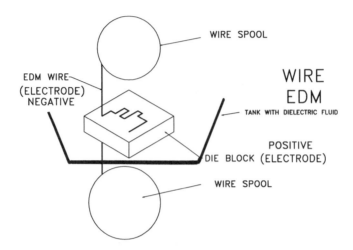

WIRE SPOOL

EDM WIRE
(ELECTRODE)
NEGATIVE

WIRE
EDM

TANK WITH DIELECTRIC FLUID

POSITIVE
DIE BLOCK (ELECTRODE)

WIRE SPOOL

Fig. 3-8 Basic electrical discharge machining (EDM) using wire electrode

Fig. 3-9 Extrusion dies produced using wire EDM process. Source: Crane Plastics

Cost

Extruders vary in size from bench-top laboratory models that have a plastic output of only a few ounces per hour, to the large multiple-screw production extruders that are larger than a semitrailer truck and have a plastic output of hundreds of pounds per hour.

Extrusion is a continuous process. The product of the extruder is essentially a continuous projection of a two-dimensional profile (see Fig. 3-10). This projection must be cut to length in a secondary operation to complete the product.

The cost factors in the extrusion production process are material intensive and overhead intensive. The labor component is lower than most plastic processes unless the extruded product requires a significant amount of secondary processing.

Quality

The prime quality concerns with extruded plastic are consistency of size and uniformity of plastic. For example, PVC piping may be extruded and cut into 20-foot lengths for an order that may require thousands of lengths. The first requirement is that there be no holes in the pipe wall, and, second, that the wall thickness and pipe diameter be within specification. To ensure outside diameter control of profiles, the extrusion industry has incorporated closed-

Fig. 3-10 Extruded profiles. Source: Crane Plastics

loop laser micrometers that can continuously measure the entire production run and signal the die to alter its diameter immediately if a dimensional concern is noted.

Plastic insulated wire has a quality concern regarding electrical shock, and a direct path from the outside of the wire to the conductor is a serious problem. Wire manufacturers incorporate a spark test that continuously monitors the electrical resistance of wire insulation. If a problem is noted, it will either be corrected by automatic die adjustments or the line will be shut down.

Future

The future of the extrusion industry will be defined by the consumer and the extruder manufacturers. Currently, the three main extruder manufacturing companies are located in the United States, Japan, and Germany. The sophisticated requirements of the extruded product (see Fig. 3-11) will require increasingly more sophisticated process controls to ensure product uniformity. The major markets for extruded products will remain:

- Packaging
- Building and construction
- Electric and electronics

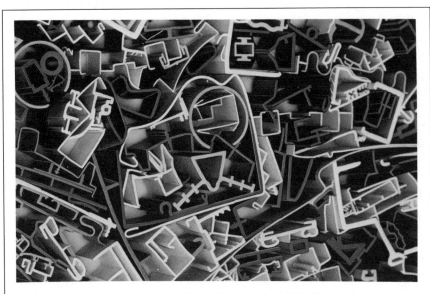

Fig. 3-11 Sophisticated extruded products. Source: Crane Plastics

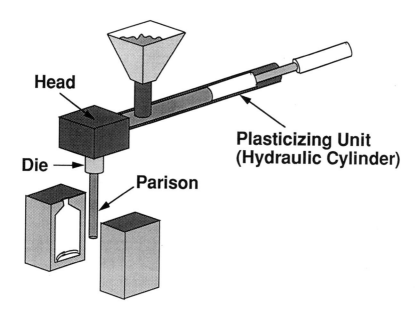

Fig. 3-12 Ram extrusion—blow molding used primarily in the 1960's and 1970's

The basic extruder will also be integrated into other processes to a greater degree. Extruders combined with thermoformers will provide manufacturers with a complete processing system to meet the packaging demands of the future. The wire and cable industry will employ extruders to process more complex plastic materials that can sustain higher voltage, lower interference, and higher temperatures. Finally, the building and construction markets will move towards plastic pipe for both pressure (incoming water supply) and drainage. These markets will also put more emphasis on co-extruded products that provide multiple advantages versus single plastic products.

Blow Molding

Blow molding is a plastic process used to manufacture hollow objects, such as containers and bottles. The blow molding process evolved from the extrusion process, as shown in Fig. 3-12 and 3-13. An extruder is used to plasticize the plastic material and extrude it into a tubular profile, referred to as a parison. The parison drops in a vertical fashion from the extruder die. The

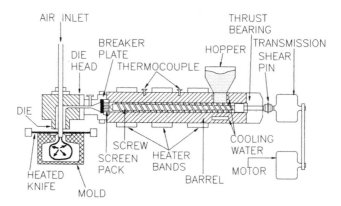

Fig. 3-13 Screw extruder—blow molder

mold, in this case a symmetrical bottle, clamps around the parison, pinching both ends and leaving the parison trapped in the mold. Next a blow pin or needle is inserted into the mold and penetrates the entrapped plastic parison, which is still hot. Air is forced through the needle at 90 to 120 psi, and the parison expands to assume the shape of the inside of the mold, which renders the outside of the bottle. The blow-molded part is allowed to cool and thus harden inside the closed mold so that when the mold is opened a rigid container can eject. See Fig. 3-14.

The beauty of blow molding lies in its simplicity. In the 1960's, blow-molded containers were mainly high-density polyethylene (HDPE) and were used almost exclusively for laundry products such as liquid soaps and bleaches. In the late 1960's, federally approved grades of HDPE were developed, and glass bottles started to yield to the lighter weight and safer plastic bottles. An added advantage of the blow-molded milk bottle was that the simple process could be incorporated adjacent to the pasteurization and homogenization units at dairies, allowing bottles to be made on demand and in place. The temperatures that were used to mold the plastic bottles also provided the dairy with sterile containers without any additional washing operation. Needless to say, glass bottles could not compete.

In the early 1970's, the glass bottle industry found itself under attack again. This time it was by the multimillion dollar "pop" bottle industry. The Achilles'

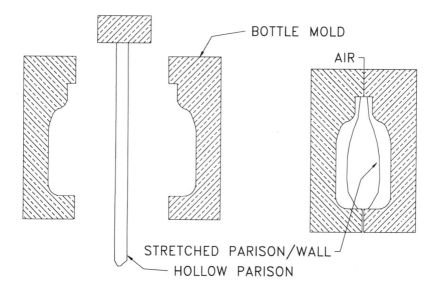

Fig. 3-14 Basic blow molding principle

heel for most plastics was the fact that all plastics used for blow-molded containers up to this time could not hold the gas and maintain the pressure required to keep the fizz in the soda. The soft drink manufacturers worked closely with the plastic manufacturers and developed a series of low gas permeable materials that meet all the requirements. The material that was finally developed is polyethylene terephthalate (PET), a thermoplastic polyester that now dominates the soft drink bottle market.

One more detail that had to be resolved before the all-plastic, blow-molded soft drink bottle would satisfy the customer as a better-than-glass replacement: the bottle cap! The conventional metal bottle cap that was used with glass bottles for decades would not work with the plastic bottle. The plastic had a tendency to yield, expand, contract, and render the metal cap ineffective. Container experts decided that a threaded cap could be designed to meet the needs and provide the customer with the ability to reseal the container, a feature not available with the metal caps on glass bottles.

In order for the threaded cap to be effective on the plastic bottle, the plastic bottle had to have a rigid neck and quality threads, which are attributes not normally associated with a conventionally blow-molded bottle.

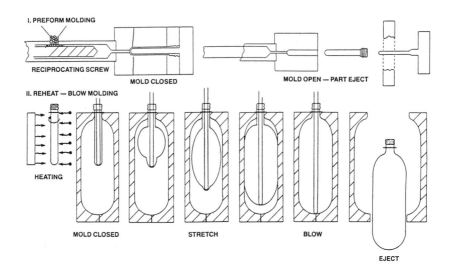

Fig. 3-15 Stretch blow molding process. Source: Johnson Controls and Goodyear Tire and Rubber Co.

Processors knew that injection molding could provide the necessary neck and thread requirements and blow molding could provide the necessary bottle component. The result was a hybrid process known as stretch blow molding, a variation of injection blow molding.

The first step is to injection mold a rigid test-tube with the required thread details. This is called the preform. The preform is then transported to the location where it is to be blow molded. The preform is conditioned or pre-heated, then inserted into a conventional-looking blow mold where air is injected and the rest of the soda bottle is formed. See Fig. 3-15 and 3-16.

Typical Blow-Molded Products

Blow-molded products are noted for their hollow configuration, and recent advances in processing technology and tooling have resulted in the use of the blow molding process for manufacturing:

- Bottles and containers (see Fig. 3-17)
- Pressure vessels
- Automobile gas tanks (see Fig. 3-18)
- Toys
- Shipping containers (up to 50 gallons)

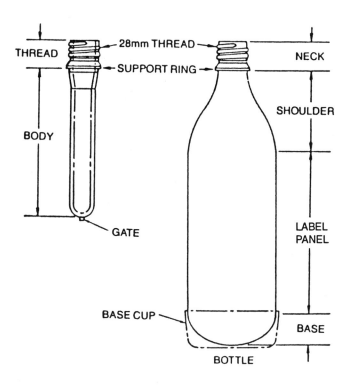

THREAD

28mm THREAD

SUPPORT RING

NECK

BODY

SHOULDER

GATE

LABEL
PANEL

BASE CUP

BASE

BOTTLE

Fig. 3-16 Typical preform and stretch blow-molded bottle. Source: Johnson Controls and Goodyear Tire and Rubber Co.

The size of the blow-molded product is limited by the output of the extruder and the complexity of the die; however, computer-controlled parison extruders allow the manufacturer to vary parison size, shape, and rate of extrusion to increase part complexity.

Tooling

Blow molding tooling is not subjected to the high clamping and material pressures found in most other plastic processes. The air pressure used to inflate the parison in the mold is standard shop air, less than 120 psi, and the clamp systems to hold the molds closed are much lower than for compression and injection molding processes. This processing environment allows the blow molds to be made of aluminum, instead of tool steel. The aluminum mold is only a fraction of the expense of an equivalent steel mold, and the aluminum provides better heat transfer, which means the blow-molded plastic part will cool more quickly and thus cycle times will be faster.

Fig. 3-17 Blow-molded containers. Source: Bekum Mfg.

The blow mold or blow molding machine will usually include a blow pin that enters the mold, penetrates the parison, and injects air to inflate the parison. Also characteristic of the blow mold are ample numbers of vents located all along the parting line of the mold. Several vents are required to allow the mold air on the outside of the parison to escape as the parison (which is sometimes called the preform) inflates.

The injection blow molding tooling is more complicated than the conventional blow molds, and there are two distinct tooling requirements. First, an injection mold is required in the injection portion of the process. This mold will have the external thread-making mechanism for the resealable cap, and the mold will be made of tool steel. Second, the mold may be made of either steel or aluminum in the blow portion of the process. In the 2-liter soft drink container industry, steel has recently been the metal of choice because of its durability and its ability to be highly polished, thus imparting the clear, smooth surface demanded by that market.

Cost

Cost factors associated with the blow molding industry fall into two distinct categories: processing and transportation.

The processing cost is directly related to the cycle time of the process and the number of blow-molded items, *i.e.*, the number of mold cavities, that can be molded at one time from one machine. Most production machines can

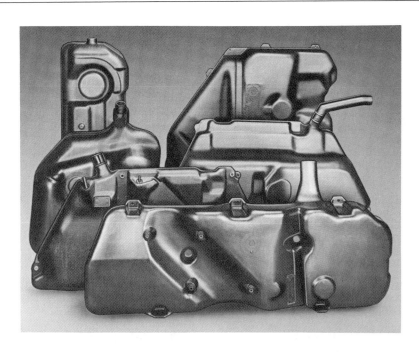

Fig. 3-18 Blow-molded fuel tanks. Source: Bekum Mfg.

accommodate multiple cavities and the process is continuous and automatic. Very little intervention is required of an operator in the blow molding process.

The waste associated with the blow-molded product is minimal. The pinch-off waste (see Fig. 3-19) is common in conventional blow molding. This waste may be reground and fed back to the blow molder. The injection blow molding waste is zero as designed by the process.

Transportation is a cost factor that is more predominant in blow-molded products because the products are usually hollow. The hollow shape means that the shipping density or the amount of product that can be loaded in any container or truck is low, which increases the shipping cost. This high transportation cost has motivated many companies to develop captive blow molding facilities within their manufacturing sites to manufacture products as required. The high cost of transportation has also inspired entrepreneurs to develop small blow molding facilities near larger manufacturers to service their needs.

Quality

The primary quality issue associated with blow-molded products is the uniformity of the container wall thickness. Historically, blow-molded container walls have been dependent on the parison wall thicknesss, the complexity and size of the part to be molded (or how much the parison must stretch), and the ability of the plastic itself to stretch and yield. The programmable parison and special blow molding grades of plastic have reduced the

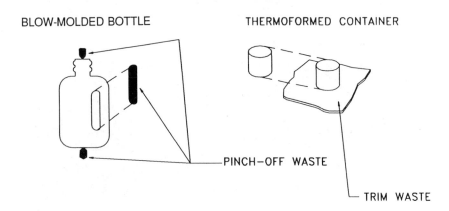

Fig. 3-19 Blow molding pinch off waste

wall thickness issues and provided product designers with greater latitude in terms of both product size and complexity when using the blow molding process.

Future

The future of the blow molding process is going to be impacted by consumer issues, such as recycling. Those factors that increase the cost of transporting blow-molded products also affect the disposal of the product. Landfills, already at a critical stage, are making overtures not to accept hollow blow-molded products. In order to survive, the blow molding industry is taking an aggressive position on recycling, from both the manufacturer's and the consumer's standpoint.

All the plastic used by the blow molding process can be recycled if properly identified and sorted.

Blow molding technology will continue to be enhanced by computer process control and by integration with other processes. The pressure vessel segment of the blow-molded market will expand to include more metal-to-plastic conversion of fuel, water, and chemical storage tanks.

Many blow molders feel that in addition to the container markets, structural blow-molded parts will be an important market of the future.

Injection Molding

As mentioned earlier, extrusion uses the most plastic material; however, injection molding is the largest volume plastic processing technique for the mass production of plastic parts with complex, three-dimensional shapes.

Injection molding comes to most people's minds when considering plastic processes because injection-molded parts are the most visible to the average consumer. Injection-molded plastic parts are the most likely to replace existing metal, wood, or glass parts.

The variations of injection molding are many; some of the main variations are:

- Thermoplastic injection molding
- Thermoset injection molding
- Multicolor injection molding
- Insert or overmolding
- Elastomer/rubber injection molding
- Liquid injection molding
- Structural foam injection molding
- Injection-compression molding

Fig. 3-20 Modern 550-ton U.S. injection molding machine. Source: Husky Injection Molding Systems Ltd., Bolton, Ontario, Canada

To simplify the discussion, only the basic injection molding of thermoplastic and thermosetting materials is discussed.

Concept

The injection molding process is a machine-oriented process (see Fig. 3-20) that can be described in basic terms as the high-pressure injection of a specific amount of plastic material into a clamped mold.

The original injection molding machines were developed in Germany prior to World War II and consisted of heated cylinders that melted the plastic and plungers that were used as rams to force the melted plastic into small molds. The sophistication of the machines did not change much until after World War II, when the demand for consumer goods dramatically increased and the development of low-cost plastic materials was a reality. The injection molding machine maintained its plunger format until the development and marketing of the reciprocating screw injection molding machine in the late 1950's and early 1960's. The rising use of the reciprocating screw injection molding machine led to the significant growth of the plastic industry that started in the 1960's and continues today.

The basic components and operation of the reciprocating screw injection molding machine can be seen in Fig. 3-21 and 3-22.

The modern injection molding machine can be described best as consisting of two distinct parts that work together, the clamp unit and the injection unit.

The clamp unit is the portion of the injection machine, also called a mold press, that holds the mold closed during the high-pressure injection of the plastic melt. To accomplish this task, the clamp unit holds the mold in position by having the mold mounted on two platens. One of the platens (the one closest to the injection unit) does not move and is called the stationary platen.

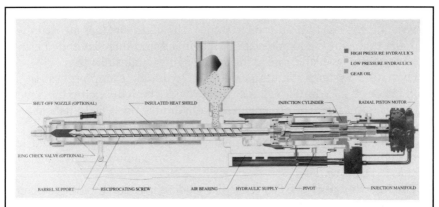

Fig. 3-21 Hydromechanical clamp system. Source: Husky Injection Molding Systems Ltd., Bolton, Ontario, Canada

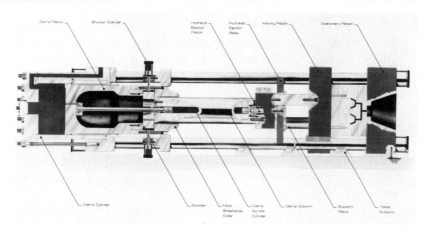

Fig. 3-22 Reciprocating screw injection unit. Source: Husky Injection Molding Systems, Ltd., Bolton, Ontario, Canada

The other platen moves to allow the mold to open and close; it is referred to as the movable platen.

The clamping mechanisms used to generate the high force needed to keep the mold closed fall into two major categories: toggle systems and hydraulic systems.

Toggle Systems. Toggle mold presses use the mechanical advantage of a linkage machine to create the high forces. The key advantages of toggle clamp machines are that they are faster (clamp movement) and require less energy because there is less hydraulic oil to pump. The disadvantages are that there are more points in the toggle clamp to maintain and there is limited clamp pressure control available due to the nature of the toggle linkages.

Hydraulic Systems. Simply stated, the hydraulic clamping system for mold presses is a hydraulic cylinder that provides both the clamp movement and the clamp force. The advantages of a hydraulic press lie in its ability to precisely control a wide range of clamp forces and in its simplicity. The disadvantages of hydraulic mold presses are that they are considered less energy efficient than toggle presses due to the large amount of hydraulic oil that has to be moved.

The injection unit (see Fig. 3-23) of a modern injection molding machine looks much like an extruder and is often referred to as the extruder in some countries. The simplest way to describe the functions of the injection unit is to describe them in terms of their effect on the plastic material:

1. Thermoplastic pellets enter the throat of the injection unit. The throat is maintained at a temperature that keeps the plastic from melting.
2. As the plastic enters the throat, it falls onto and between the flights of the rotating screw. The screw is turning in a direction that augers the plastic pellets forward.
3. As the screw advances the plastic into the injection barrel, the material is subjected to a significant amount of shear, or frictional forces. These shear forces generate heat. The frictional heat and heat supplied by external heaters melt the thermoplastic material. The temperature of the melt is controlled by heater bands, the screw speed, and the back pressure.
4. The screw is still turning and the plastic is still advancing forward, picking up heat and melting as it goes.
5. Toward the front third of the injection unit the plastic is completely melted. The shape of the screw changes (see Fig. 3-24) toward the front, and the root of the screw gets larger, thus allowing less plastic between the screw and the barrel wall. This narrowing is called the metering zone and provides the injection unit precise control of material volume that is moved in front of the screw.
6. The plastic melt continues its journey toward the front of the screw by passing through a check valve. This valve is usually in the form of a slip ring or ball check, and it allows plastics to pass by it in only one direction: toward the front of the screw.

7. After passing by the check valve, the melt is deposited in front of the screw. This area is called the shooting pot because it will be the next shot, or next material to be injected into the mold. As the plastic melt is deposited in front of the screw, it forces the screw to move backward. The screw will continue to rotate and auger plastic forward, while at the same time being pushed rearward. The rearward motion of the screw is defined by the preset limit switch, which, in effect, defines the precise amount of plastic melt to be allowed into the shooting pot.

8. The final action of the screw is to move forward at a defined speed and pressure and force the plastic melt, which has been deposited in the shooting pot, into the closed mold. The screw does not rotate during the injection process. After the plastic melt is injected into the mold, the part cools, the mold opens, and the part is ejected. The process is repeated to create and inject the next shot.

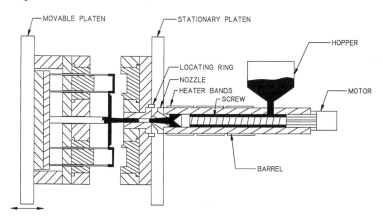

Fig. 3-23 Reciprocating screw injection molding machine

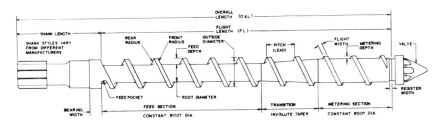

Fig. 3-24 Injection screw. Source: Spirex Corp.

This reciprocating, or back and forth, action of the screw gives the injection molding process the name reciprocating screw injection molding.

The clamping unit, whether it is a toggle system or a hydraulic system, is "married" to the injection unit of the injection molding machine physically and logically. The sequences of the clamp unit are:

1. The clamping system closes the mold in a controlled manner and creates a clamp force that exceeds the force of the injected plastic.
2. The plastic is injected.
3. The mold remains clamped until the plastic has cooled and solidified.
4. The mold opens in a controlled manner.
5. The molding machine activates the ejector system of the mold to eject the part.
6. The cycle is repeated.

Typical Injection-Molded Parts

Injection-molded parts usually have the most complex geometries of any plastic molding process. This provides the designer with infinite design possibilities (see Fig. 3-25) including the ability to replace existing products that are made of nonplastic materials. Some examples of injection-molded parts include:

- Auto battery cases
- Computer/printer housings
- Disposable razors
- Plastic closures (bottle caps)
- Eyeglass frames
- Auto taillights
- Plastic cutlery
- Soles for athletic shoes

The types and varieties of products that are injection molded are infinite.

Tooling

The complexity of injection-molded plastic parts requires molds of equal complexity. Molds may vary in size according to the part size to be molded and the number of cavities within one mold. Some molds are as small as 3 in. by 3 in. or as large as 10 ft. by 10 ft. The mold cost also may vary from $5000 to $500,000.

The objective of any injection mold is to produce a quality part, with no wasted material, in an economical cycle time.

Fig. 3-25 Typical injection-molded parts

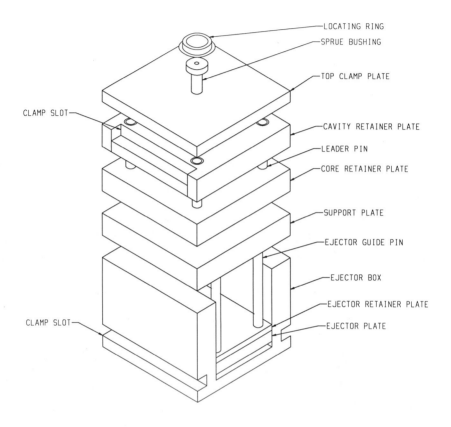

Fig. 3-26 Exploded view of mold

The construction of molds varies, but the basic injection mold is considered as a model in both construction and nomenclature. See Fig. 3-26 and 3-27.

Injection mold technology has been a good reflection of the world-class manufacturing revolution that has impacted manufacturing facilities around the globe. Injection molds are being designed for quick mold changes (QMC) by standardizing mold installation procedures. Also, injection molds are becoming more productive and less wasteful by molding quality plastic parts automatically and reducing or eliminating material waste. Figure 3-28 illustrates the evolution of mold improvement by the reduction of nonproductive material generated by the mold.

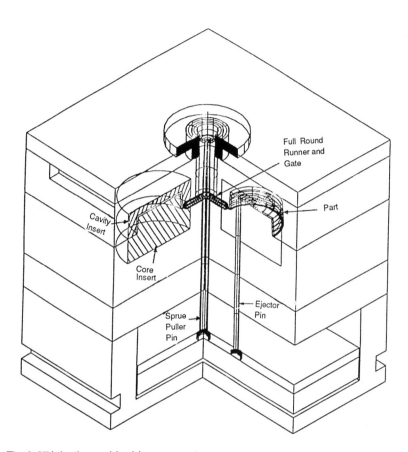

Fig. 3-27 Injection mold cold runner system

Cost

Injection-molded product cost has to be considered from two perspectives:

1. The actual cost of the molded part itself
2. The value of the injection-molded part in an assembly

The cost of the injection-molded part is a function of the material used, the process cycle time, and the overhead associated with the process. Injection molding may be considered a continuous batch process. It is continuous from

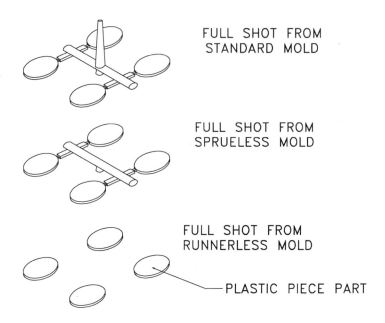

FULL SHOT FROM
STANDARD MOLD

FULL SHOT FROM
SPRUELESS MOLD

FULL SHOT FROM
RUNNERLESS MOLD

PLASTIC PIECE PART

Fig. 3-28 Injection-molded shot evolution

the standpoint that most injection molding processes are automatic, and it is batch from the standpoint that each cycle is a new event with possible changes in variables and products.

The sophisticated closed-loop microprocessor control systems are able to make rapid process adjustments to compensate for process variations, and the result is closer tolerances and more consistent product quality.

The other area of cost concern is the debate between large, multiple cavity molds and molding the same product simultaneously on two or more presses that have smaller molds with fewer cavities. The latter scenario is considered to offer the most production flexibility both in terms of process maintenance and being able to support just in time (JIT) production demands.

Quality

Approximately 50% of the injection presses currently in use are over 15 years old and do not have the advanced electronic process control logic of the new processing equipment. This is not to say that the older processes cannot produce good parts. In fact, the issues may be seen in reverse, *i.e.*, the newer, high tech processes may lull the processor into believing that the quality of his product is built into the technology of the machine.

The quality of the injection-molded product rests on the ability of the processor to control all the process variables regardless of the type of equipment used. These variables include:

- Incoming material
- Tooling
- Machine variables
- Operator (human) variables

In addition to the above, product quality depends on the condition of the equipment. Preventive maintenance is a cornerstone of injection-molded part quality.

Future

Injection molding will grow and develop from three distinct global areas:

- United States/Canada
- Pacific Rim (Japan/Korea)
- Europe (Germany/Austria)

The advances in injection molding technology will be in the area of total factory automation or "lights out manufacturing." Those issues that have plagued injection molding in the past, such as plastic material variation, mold quality, and machine process controls, are already targeted for development. The competitive nature of the global market will squeeze the lower quality equipment into extinction, and there is the threat that small custom mold making facilities will yield to high tech computerized mold making. There is already a decreasing trend in average age and experience of mold makers throughout the world that has been brought about by the use of numerically controlled machines for tool and die manufacturing.

In the future, molds will be purchased from overseas with as much ease as they are purchased domestically mainly due to the world standardization of design software and tooling components. This, combined with the increased ease of global communications (verbal and graphic), will dissolve any remaining barriers left in the global marketplace.

Thermoforming

Thermoforming, also referred to as vacuum forming, is a plastic process that begins with plastic sheet as the starting material. The plastic sheet is placed in a clamp frame (see Fig. 3-29) to hold it securely on all edges. Thermal energy, usually in the form of convection and radiant heat from electric heating elements, is applied for a sufficient amount of time to soften the plastic sheet. Once the sheet material is sufficiently softened, a mold is brought into contact

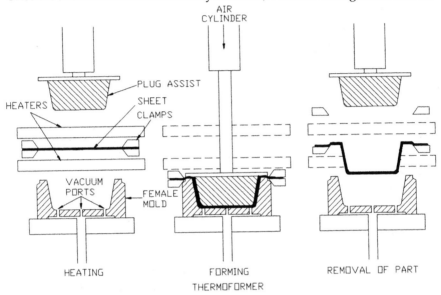

Fig. 3-29 Basic thermoforming process steps

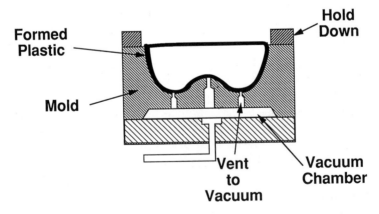

Fig. 3-30 Straight vacuum forming

with the sheet, and a vacuum is applied that draws the softened sheet toward
the mold to mirror the configuration of the mold. See Fig. 3-30. After the sheet
cools, it will retain the shape of the mold when the mold is removed. Figure
3-31 shows a basic thermoformer.

Historically, thermoforming has been considered a one-sided process, *i.e.,*
the softened sheet will either mirror a male mold and have the inside become
the critical surface and the outside the noncritical surface, or mirror a female

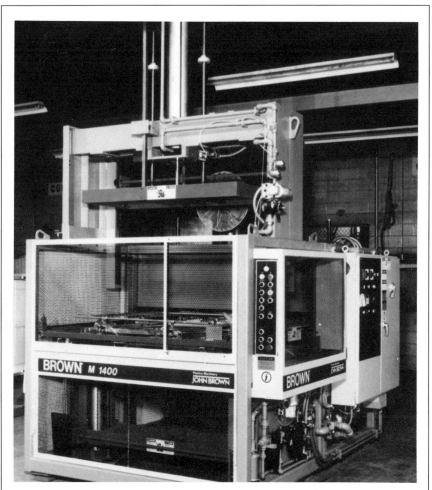

Fig. 3-31 Basic thermoformer. Source: Brown Machine Div., Beaverton, MI

mold and have the outside be the critical surface and the inside become the noncritical surface.

This one-sided approach to thermoforming was satisfactory for decades when the process was used primarily for simple packaging parts. Today, the thermoforming process has advanced to include molded products that have two critical sides and dimensional accuracy that allows the thermoformed part to be used in key automotive and building and construction applications.

Typical Thermoformed Parts

The majority of thermoformed products are in the packaging market; however, broader applications include (see Fig. 3-32 and 3-33):

- Blister packages
- Foam food containers
- Refrigerator and dishwasher door liners
- Auto interior panels
- Tub/shower shells, which are later fiber reinforced
- Pickup truck bed liners
- Lighted acrylic and cellulose acetate butyrate (CAB) signs

Tooling

The thermoforming process offers some unique tooling advantages over other conventional plastic processes, primarily because the thermoform molds are relatively simple in design and construction.

Prototypes, using the thermoforming process, afford the part designer and manufacturer the opportunity to make simple molds quickly using inexpensive materials, such as wood, plaster, and epoxy. Many designers will insist upon a product design review that includes one or more thermoformed prototypes that will allow a reasonable assessment of product form, fit, and function.

Many manufacturers will also produce their initial production runs on low-cost thermoforming molds until the product matures. Later, the product could be embellished, requiring that the process and production tooling become those of an injection molding format.

The tooling materials for prototype thermoform molds include:

- Wood
- Plaster
- Gypsum
- Epoxy

Fig. 3-32 Thermoformed containers. Source: Brown Machine Div., Beaverton, MI

Fig. 3-33 Thermoformed boat hull and liner. Source: Brown Machine Div., Beaverton, MI

The tooling materials acceptable for low-volume, under 500 parts, production include:

- Epoxy
- Beryllium copper
- Aluminum

Most high-volume production molds for the thermoforming process are made using cast and/or machined aluminum.

The tooling designs vary, but some standard thermoforming mold concepts include (see Fig. 3-34):

- Male molds
- Female molds
- Plug-assisted female molds
- Matched molds

The thermoform mold also includes a number of small (0.032 to 0.063 in. diameter) holes that are strategically machined on and around the mold details to provide the required vacuum or negative pressure used to form the soft plastic sheet against the mold surface. Also required is a vacuum distribution box beneath the mold to ensure that the vacuum is distributed to all the vacuum holes in the mold.

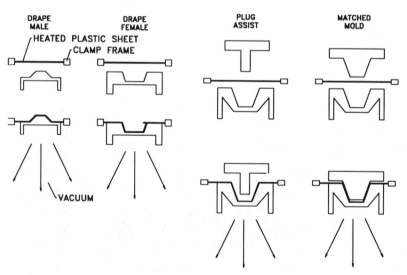

Fig. 3-34 Four basic thermoforming techniques

Cost

Thermoforming is one of the lowest cost plastic processes. The equipment required is relatively simple in design and operation.

The tooling is simple and low-cost when compared to other plastic processes because of the low pressures involved and the low abrasion of the plastic.

The expense of the thermoforming process is directly related to the material cost, both from the extruded plastic sheet that is the starting raw material to the wasted material that is generated because the plastic sheet must be held in a clamping frame. This material can be regranulated and processed.

The labor content in the thermoforming process is also considered to be higher than other plastic processes because there is often operator involvement to handle raw material or to trim the formed sheet.

Note that thermoforming has two distinct markets, with separate cost structures.

The high-volume packaging markets (see Fig. 3-35) utilize thermoformers that are integrated directly with sheet extruders, and the product is automatically cut from the formed sheet stock. This thermoforming is the lowest in cost.

The lower volume nonpackaging markets that use thermoforming mainly due to its ability to produce large plastic parts will be significantly higher in labor and material costs.

Fig. 3-35 Automatic in-line thermoforming packaging. Source: Brown Machine Div., Beaverton, MI

Quality

The quality of thermoformed plastic parts depends on the type of mold used, the type of plastic used, and the method of thermoforming.

Molds. A thermoformed part manufactured on a female mold tends to have a wall thickness that varies by becoming thinner as the plastic is drawn into the the mold because the area of plastic sheet available to form a part on a female mold is only a small percentage of the area of the formed part. Parts molded using male molds may have thin sections in the opposite areas compared to parts molded using female molds.

Thermoforming processes can reduce this dramatic wall thickness variation by using techniques such as plug-assisted molding.

Molds for thermoforming must also have very liberal radii (no sharp edges), to enable the plastic to conform to the mold more easily.

Material. The sheet plastic used for thermoforming has a major impact on the thermoform process. Some plastic materials, like polycarbonate, have to be dried prior to thermoforming because they are hygroscopic (absorb moisture) and the moisture will weaken the plastic part.

Amorphous plastics such as ABS, styrene, and cellulose acetate butyrate (CAB) are excellent forming plastics because they maintain their heat and stretch well. Crystalline plastics, such as polyethylene and nylon, are more difficult to thermoform because they do not have a wide processing temperature window.

Styrene-based plastics, such as polystyrene, ABS, and polystyrene foam, are the most widely used thermoforming plastics.

Method. The method or technique used to thermoform plastic parts affects the part quality. Manually produced thermoformed parts will have a wider variation in part quality than automatically thermoformed parts.

Thermoform molds that are heated produce a better match to the surface quality of the mold because the heat is maintained for a longer period of time.

Finally, the secondary operations, such as trimming, printing, and assembly, will impact product quality.

Future

Thermoforming will continue to be primarily used in the packaging markets; however, the use of thermoformed shells or exteriors that are subsequently reinforced with fiberglass will make a more pronounced impact on the building and construction market (tubs/showers and building panels) and the automobile market (interior/exterior body panels), which have been served by the sheet metal market.

▼ Plastics in combination with structures

▼ Reinforcements

▼ The highest strength to weight material

- Fiberglass

- Kevlar Composites

- Graphite Composites

Fig. 3-36 Composite plastics. Note: Kevlar is a tradename of Du Pont for aramid fiber

Composite Plastic Processing

Composite plastics can be either thermoplastic or thermosetting materials that are reinforced with glass fibers, graphite fibers, or other materials with the specific objective of increasing the strength of the material. See Fig. 3-36.

The nature of the composite material lends itself to a wide variety of hand-oriented and machine-oriented processes.

Hand-oriented processes include:

- Hand lay-ups
- Casting
- Spray lay-ups

Machine-oriented processes include:

- Matched compression molding
- Injection molding
- Filament winding
- Pultrusion
- Structural reaction injection molding (SRIM)
- Resin transfer molding (RTM)

Hand lay-up is a manual composite process that requires skill, patience, and a good knowledge of the glass reinforcements and plastic material used as the matrix.

The plastic materials used in hand lay-ups are usually unsaturated poly-ester resin, vinyl ester resin, or epoxy resin. These materials are thermosetting viscous liquids that require a catalyst or hardener to initiate their cure. After the catalyst has been added and mixed, the individual doing the lay-up has about 15 to 25 minutes to work with the plastic before it sets or cures.

The lay-up procedure consists of creating several layers of glass reinforce-ment, usually in the form of a mat or cloth, and wetting it with the catalyzed resin. The wetted reinforcement is layered into or onto a form or mold that has been prepared with a release agent. The pattern and order of the layering is critical to the final shape and strength of the product.

After the layering is complete, the entire system is allowed to cure for several hours. After the cure is complete, the part can be removed from the mold.

Hand lay-up is a slow, low-volume production process that is excellent for low-volume, large structural parts, such as:

- Boat hulls
- Custom auto bodies
- Homemade aircraft

The hand lay-up process may also incorporate a layer of plastic foam sheet sandwiched between two exterior surfaces of glass and resin. This sandwich composite structure affords the product designer an improved strength-to-weight ratio.

For high technology composite applications, such as aircraft components, reinforcement impregnated with epoxy, called prepeg, is used.

Prepegs are cured by vacuum bag molding in which the hand-crafted prepeg part is placed into a bag made of a heat-resistant plastic film. The entire part is placed into an oven, and a vacuum is pulled on the part while the heat of the oven cures the resin. Many such parts have foamed or honeycomb cores with surface skins of carbon/epoxy.

Casting. The casting of composite plastic materials is dominated by epoxy resin and reinforcements that include both glass (fiber and particle) and metal.

Advances in the strength of casting epoxy composites have created oppor-tunities for them to be used in these applications:

- Thermoform and prototype molds
- Short-run stamping dies
- Check fixtures for plastic and metal parts

Spray lay-ups are very similar to hand lay-ups with the exception that spray lay-ups employ a chopper gun that has these functions:

- Feeds the resin
- Feeds the catalyst
- Feeds the glass fiber and chops the glass into short (1- to 2-in. strands)

All these components are sprayed on the mold or onto the form surface and allowed to cure. The spray lay-up technique allows the processor to manufacture products in higher volumes and at a lower cost than conventional, hand lay-up operations. The disadvantage of this process is that it results in a lower percentage of fiberglass, and therefore, produces a heavier product.

The end-use markets for spray lay-up are the same as those for hand lay-up.

Matched-die compression molding of composite plastic materials is similar to conventional compression molding with the exception of the starting material.

Composite material is in the form of sheet molding compound (SMC), which is polyester resin soaked into glass mat, or bulk molding compound (BMC), which is polyester resin reinforcement, and 30 to 40% filler in the form of a dough consistency and shaped into the form of rope or logs. The BMC or SMC is inserted into heated molds where it is compressed and cured.

Typical applications for the matched-die compression molding process include:

- Cafeteria trays
- Auto body panels
- Commercial aircraft interior panels

Injection molding of composite plastics is virtually identical to the standard injection molding process. The composite materials, in this case, can be either thermoset or thermoplastic. The process of injection molding heavily reinforced plastic materials creates a great deal of abrasion and wear on both the molding machine and the mold, decreasing the useful life of both.

Injection moldable composites are referred to as glass- or mineral-filled materials and are used in high volumes. Composite injection-molded plastic parts are normally used for applications that require higher strength or higher temperature resistance, or for applications that were previously serviced by metal. The addition of glass fibers also affects the thermal expansion and modulus of elasticity (stiffness) of thermoplastics.

Filament winding is a composite process that is primarily used to manufacture large structural containers or tanks. The process involves several spools

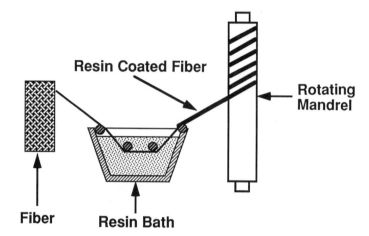

Thermoset Process

Use: Creating high stiffness components, shafts, and tanks

Fig. 3-37 Filament-winding system

of reinforcing glass strands, or other reinforcing materials, being directed into a resin bath, which is mostly polyester. The wetted strands are then wound over a turning mandrel (see Fig. 3-37) in different patterns to provide different strengths. After the resin has cured, the filament wound part is removed from the mandrel and machined or assembled as required.

Some key applications for filament wound composites include:

- Gasoline storage tanks for service stations
- Septic tanks
- Large diameter drainage pipe for culverts
- Chemical storage systems
- Sporting equipment, such as golf club shafts and bike frames

Pultrusion is a composite process that has many similarities to the extrusion process, including the sound of its name. As in the filament winding process, the pultrusion process begins with strands of fiber reinforcements that are wetted in a resin tank. However, the next step in the process is to pull the resin-soaked strands through a long heated die. The die may be in the shape of a rod, tube, I-beam, or other geometric shape.

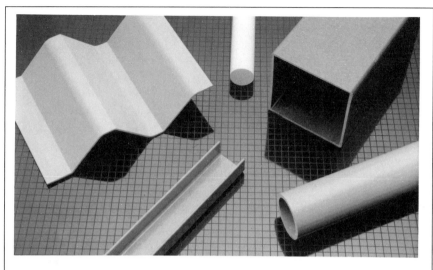

Fig. 3-38 Pultruded products—structural beams. Source: Coastal Engineering Products, Inc.

After the resin is cured and pulled through the die, the resulting profile has a high strength-to-weight ratio and is very durable, especially in a chemical environment.

Applications for pultruded products include:

- Structural beams for chemical environments (Fig. 3-38)
- Poles and shafts (Fig. 3-39)

The future of the pultrusion process may be in space applications where long structural components for space stations could be manufactured in place as required, eliminating the need to transport long beams from earth.

Structural reaction injection molding (SRIM) is a composite process that evolved from reaction injection molding (RIM). The SRIM process involves delivering two reactants and a reinforcement into a mixing chamber just prior to injecting the mixture into a closed mold. The reactants, often polyurethane, epoxy, or polyester, are injected into a mold where they polymerize or cure, embedding the reinforcement. The cured part is a structurally strong and durable item.

The advantage of SRIM is that very large, structurally sound, molded parts can be fabricated using low-pressure equipment and low-cost tooling.

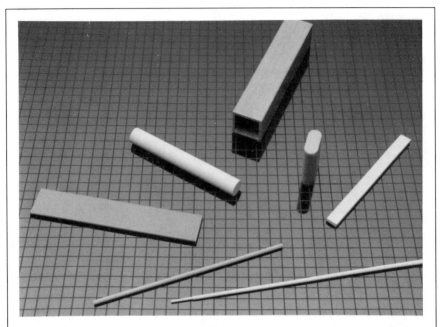

Fig. 3-39 Pultruded profiles—poles and shafts. Source: Coastal Engineering Products, Inc.

Typical SRIM applications include:

- Auto body exterior panels
- Large bins and containers

The SRIM process is in its infancy. SRIM manufactured products will soon enter the building and construction, furniture, and recreational vehicle markets.

Resin transfer molding (RTM) is a composite process that provides the manufacturer the opportunity to select and locate the exact shape and position of the reinforcement in the product. The glass reinforcement is in a mat configuration. This mat is cut, shaped, and placed into the desired position in an open mold. The mold is closed, and the liquid resin is injected at a rate that will fill the mold but not disturb the shape and position of the reinforcement.

This added control is attractive both to both product designers and to manufacturers, who, up to this time, have had to rely on random flow of resin and reinforcement to achieve a reinforced part.

Typical applications for RTM include:

- Truck cab shells
- Auto exterior panels
- Recreational vehicle exteriors

The processing of plastic materials is one of the broadest subjects in today's manufacturing environment. The challenge for the plastic product designer and the plastic manufacturer is to remain current in terms of new processing technology. Simultaneous advances in plastic materials and plastic processing technology will result in manufacturing sites that have to adapt rapidly to meet the market demands. The plastic product designer will be challenged to understand the full breadth of plastics processing technology and to accommodate product designs with the appropriate design criteria to use the processes successfully.

4

Economics of Plastics

Previous chapters mention the importance of understanding the plastic materials to be used in specific product designs and of understanding the process by which a plastic product is to be manufactured. The next step is to recognize the type of design effort that is required for a plastic product.

Types of Design Efforts

Whether the product is going to be one plastic part or a system with several plastic parts, there are four main plastic part design scenarios (see Fig. 4-1):

- New product
- Product variation
- Product cost reduction
- Material conversion

New Product

The new product design scenario is one in which there will be no precedent or similar product to use as an example. New product design is an adventure from the standpoint that new materials, design concepts, or end-use environments may have to be explored.

New product designs will require more testing, pilot runs, sample marketing, and refining than other design scenarios.

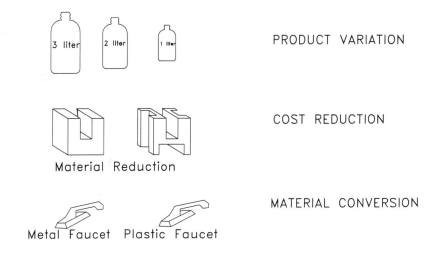

PRODUCT VARIATION

COST REDUCTION

Material Reduction

MATERIAL CONVERSION

Metal Faucet   Plastic Faucet

Fig. 4-1 Plastic product design categories

Product Variation

Product variation is when a designer takes an existing product and modifies its size, capacity, rating, color, quality level, cost, etc. to expand the product portfolio.

Examples include:

- A bottle manufacturer who wants to manufacture 1-liter and 3-liter bottles in addition to 2-liter products
- The electrical switch manufacturer who wishes to supply 220-volt in addition to 110-volt switches
- The computer manufacturer who would like to add both more advanced and more basic systems to the product line

The plastic design concerns involved with variations of existing products entail these key points:

1. Do not proliferate a bad design. If there is a design flaw in the original product, do not assume it will go away in the product variation.
2. Be careful of scaling. Increasing or decreasing the size of existing, successful products may turn out to be disastrous. Plastic properties are not linear; doubling the size does not always double the strength (see Chapter 5). Scaling of plastic parts usually requires a redesign effort and a retesting program.

3. Changing color may seem to be one of the major benefits of designing with plastic materials; however, understand that colorants are additives and any additive will have some effect on the properties of the plastic. Some plastics are more sensitive to the addition of colorants, especially white and black, so careful product evaluation of colored plastic parts must be performed.

Product Cost Reduction

Cost reduction efforts are the most prevalent plastic redesign activities; however, they are often perceived as standard manufacturing practices as opposed to redesigning activities.

The impetus to reduce the cost of a product is provided by the spiralling costs of raw material. Plastic is vulnerable to fluctuations in oil prices, and, therefore, plastic products are always candidates for lowering costs.

Quality improvements should also be listed as cost reductions because imperfections and design flaws cost money to screen, fix, or scrap.

Many cost reduction efforts are not passed along to the customer as price reductions; instead the cost reduction allows the plastics manufacturer to improve the profit margin of the company. As a result, the product designer must work within the "design envelope" of the existing product. This means that any changes in the design cannot be apparent to the customer in terms of form, fit, and function.

Material Conversion

Material conversions are design scenarios that involve redesigning non-plastic products, *e.g.*, metal, wood, glass, or ceramic products, to plastic products.

The designer must respect the product design envelope. In other words, the plastic product must be interchangeable with the nonplastic product. The designer must also conform to the rules of plastic product design, which are different from those of other materials.

The most common plastic part design mistake occurs when the design rules for nonplastic materials are applied to plastic design conversions.

Designing Parts to Meet the Customer's Requirements

What does the customer require? This question is, too often, not even asked.

Even today, many products are designed, manufactured, and marketed without any regard for the needs and desires of the customer. Consumer products designed without customer input may by chance satisfy a true customer need; however, it is the *perceived* need that usually makes consumer products desirable. Advertisers establish images using TV commercials, magazine ads, and billboards to stimulate desires that otherwise would be nonexistent.

Every so often a product is developed that satisfies a customer want so directly and accurately that the product is an immediate success. Examples are:

- McDonald's Egg McMuffin
- Compact discs
- VCR's and CamCorders
- Minivans
- Convertibles (on two separate occasions)
- Plastic 2-liter pop bottles

These products were not developed on day 1 and declared a success on day 2. These products were developed with considerable attention to researching and understanding what the customer wanted and designing the product and its components around those needs and desires.

Who is the customer? The plastic manufacturer may be molding parts for the end-user (the general consuming public) or molding parts to be used in the next assembly step in the manufacturing of a more complicated assembly. Regardless of who the customer is, the customer has specific requirements that must be satisfied in order for the plastic part to be acceptable. The plastic product supplier must understand and satisfy these needs.

The customer is always right. The old adage that the customer is always right has been embraced throughout the world manufacturing community. The words have been updated, but many manufacturers are essentially stating the same idea within the mission statements of their companies. For example:

- Meet the customer's requirements
- Meet or exceed the customer's specifications
- Comply with the customer's needs

It would seem sacrilegious to even suggest that the customer did not know what he or she wanted or that the customer was not always right.

Realistically, however, it should be stated that although the customer may have the best understanding of the concept of what is needed, the customer may not know the path to get the product needed for any specific application. The plastic product designer/manufacturer must educate the customer in terms of what plastics can and cannot do, thereby helping the customer understand the product/application even better. Educating the customer is also important because many people who are pursuing a product concept do not have a good understanding of basic plastics technology. It is often necessary, therefore, for the plastic molder to redesign the product to allow it to be manufactured.

The customer may not appreciate the fact that plastic products can be designed to maximize the functionality of his/her product. As an example, consider the metal tackle box. For decades the fisherman's tackle box consisted of metal shells and shelves joined together with metal hinges. The box was heavy and would rust.

Plastic shells and shelves were quickly seen by the customer as an alternative that would be light, rustproof, and even more colorful than metal. The metal hinges were not viewed as redesignable.

The customer told the product designer what was required and the plastic tackle box, with metal hinges, was created. The customer got what he wanted, but not what was really needed.

If the customer or the designer had known more about employing plastics not only to serve the principal need, but to also maximize design/material functionality, the tackle box would have been designed with an integral hinge molded of the same (polypropylene) material as the shells.

Whether it is including integral hinges in tackle boxes or combining connectors within the design of plastic printed circuit boards, the customer of plastic products may always be right, but he or she may require help to be successful.

Designing for Assembly

Plastics and plastic products offer today's manufacturer the best opportunity to design products for manufacturing and assembly (DFMA). Designing a product with respect to how it is to be assembled later is making a significant impact in all product markets. It requires the designer to work as part of a team that includes members from areas such as manufacturing and quality assurance, and it allows the team to review designs and conceive ideas that might not have originated from the designer working alone.

Snap fits, reduced part count, combining parts, and reduced secondary operations are all steps that can be incorporated in the part design, and such steps demonstrate the ability of plastics to maximize part functionality (see Chapter 10). The customer may not realize all the benefits associated with plastic part design and, again, may have to be educated in basic DFMA to appreciate plastic product assembly cost savings.

Plastic Part Suppliers

Understanding the customer of plastic parts is important; however, understanding the suppliers of plastic parts is equally important. The plastic parts supplier can have a significant impact on the quality of the parts being produced. The capability of a plastic parts supplier may be related to the nature of the manufacturing facility. The main plastic part supplier classifications include custom plastic manufacturers and captive plastic suppliers.

Custom plastic manufacturers. The custom plastic manufacturer is usually a processor with a specialty, such as injection molding, extrusion, blow molding, etc. The custom plastics manufacturer may also provide the tool, mold, or die building services. If these services are not directly obtainable, the custom processor should have the capability to subcontract them.

Assessing a custom plastics processor should include these critical points:

- **Technical expertise.** Are there sufficient technical skills present, or is there a need to subcontract portions of projects, such as design, tooling, or assembly?
- **Cleanliness/organization/control.** Are the facilities organized to minimize the risk of error in material control, processing, or tooling?
- **Quality control.** Does the processor know the quality of incoming plastic? Is there a preventive maintenance program for the tools? Are all the revisions and engineering changes controlled, and is the latest print revision on the shop floor? Are all the processes documented, and are the molding machines set up to the correct processes?
- **Response to problems.** Is the processor a partner or an enemy in terms of candid communication of problems and solutions?
- **Delivery.** Is the product delivered on time?
- **Product and customer base.** Does the processor have a wide customer and product base, or are you the largest customer?

Many custom processors will have a niche or expertise that separates them from their competitors. It is important to understand what, if any, specialties each custom supplier offers.

Captive plastic suppliers. The captive supplier is owned or directly part of a company whose prime product is not the sale of component plastic parts. The reasons for the use of captive plastic processors are:

- Maintain technical expertise
- Lower cost (Usually the product has no profit margin)
- Rapid turnaround or zero-inventory manufacturing

- Maintain proprietary product
- No other plastic processors nearby

The guidelines for reviewing a captive processor should be no different from those of a custom plastic processor; however, the captive supplier may have more forgiving criteria from which to work.

Examples of captive plastic product suppliers would include:

- The dairy that blow molds its own bottles
- The auto manufacturer that extrudes the elastomeric, or rubber-like, door seals
- The computer manufacturer that injection mold its computer cabinets

Captive versus custom suppliers. Comparing the cost of an internal (captive) supplier against the price of an external (custom) supplier may be difficult. The rule of thumb is to expect the captive supplier to be 20 to 35% below the custom supplier. This is simply the elimination of the profit factor. The true cost analysis also includes the difference in the cost of shipping, the indirect cost of problem solving, and the overhead costs associated with under-utilized equipment.

Global manufacturer. The fact that we are a global marketplace has not escaped the plastics processing sector. Many U.S. manufacturers are utilizing the Pacific Rim, Mexico, and South America to reduce the cost of some labor-intensive plastic parts. The assessment of the overseas supplier should consist of the supplier guidelines and a complete understanding of the local laws and economy of the country in which the processing is to be done. The quality of plastic products manufactured overseas can and should be no less than those produced domestically.

Part costing. One major consideration that needs to be understood when examining the cost of utilizing either a domestic or overseas plastic parts supplier is cost, specifically the relationship between tooling and piece part cost. Tooling is a capital cost, and piece part price is a direct material cost. Custom suppliers can manipulate the initial capital cost of tooling to make the start-up of a job more attractive, but the piece part price will be increased, resulting in a total increase in product cost.

Three scenarios are developed:

The following three scenarios illustrate part costing for a project that requires the manufacture of 1 million parts over the life of the project:

Scenario A: Tooling and piece part price separate

Mold price $50,000
Piece part price $0.02 20,000
                                                        Total outlay>$70,000

Scenario B: Lower tooling price

Mold price $45,000
Piece part price $0.03 30,000
                                                        Total outlay>$75,000

Scenario C: No tooling capital required

Mold price 0
Piece part price $0.06 ....$60,000
                                                        Total outlay>$60,000

If the initial capital costs are a factor in a plastic product start-up, the amortization (Scenario C) of tooling within the piece part pricing may be attractive even though the overall costs are greater.

It is assumed that the mold life will be sufficient to meet all product requirements. Note that if the tooling does not survive the entire production life of the product, the cost scenarios above will no longer be valid.

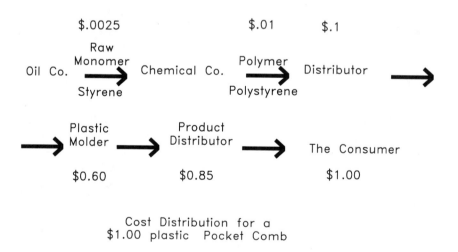

Cost Distribution for a
$1.00 plastic Pocket Comb

Fig. 4-2 Cost model of a typical plastic consumer product

Price of a Plastic Product

An example of the total cost distribution of a plastic pocket comb is illustrated in Fig. 4-2. Assume that the consumer will pay $1.00 for the comb and the actual petroleum to begin the manufacturing process costs $0.0025.

How much the customer will actually have to pay for a plastic product, of course, depends on a range of variables:

- Raw material cost ($$/pound)
- Material content (ounces/part)
- Quantity of parts to be manufactured
- Tooling (molds, dies, and fixtures)
- Quality requirements
- Delivery requirements

It is possible to generalize in order to better understand the plastic cost components. A few basic definitions are required:

Cost: Sum of the material, labor, overhead, and yield loss
Price: Total cost plus profit
Material: Cost of all materials used (*i.e.*, productive and nonproductive)
Productive material: Material that is sold as product
Nonproductive: Material that is not part of the product, but generated during the process
Labor: Total labor dollars expended in the manufacturing of the product
Overhead: Dollars expended on employee benefits (usually a function of labor dollars), depreciation, shipping, utility costs, management, building/warehouse costs
Yield loss: Unrecoverable waste incurred in the process

Table 4-1 illustrates a comparison of the relative material, labor, overhead, and yield loss (MLOY) values for different processes. It shows, for example,

Table 4-1 Plastic Product Cost Analysis

	Thermoplastic injection	Thermoset injection	Extrusion	Blow molding	Thermo-forming
M (Material)	25 to 35%	20 to 30%	70 to 80%	70 to 80%	60 to 75%
L (Labor)	25 to 35%	30 to 50%	10 to 15%	10 to 15%	15 to 25%
O (Overhead)	25 to 35%	25 to 35%	15 to 20%	15 to 20%	15 to 25%
Y (Yield)	1 to 5%	4 to 8%	1 to 2%	1 to 2%	4 to 8%

that material cost in a product runs about 25 to 35% for injection molding and 70 to 80% for extrusion.

Injection-Molded Part Costing

Injection-molded parts, *i.e.*, thermoset and thermoplastic, are among the most complicated processes to determine product cost. Figure 4-3 illustrates both a standard (productive and nonproductive material) shot and a cost-reduced, highly efficient runnerless (product only) shot. The following cost scenarios will illustrate how the same part geometry could vary as molding assumptions are altered. Only material cost per part is considered for the sake of simplicity and regrind is assumed to be available.

Scenario A

Material = Thermoplastic
Shot style = Standard (A)
Cost/lb = $2.00
Regrind allowed = None
Shot weight (per cycle) = (4 x 20 g) + (80 g) = 160 g
Part weight (material used per part) = 160 g/4 = 40 g/part, or 8.8 lb/1000 parts
Material cost = $2.00 x 8.8 = $17.6/1000 parts, or $0.176/part

Scenario B

Material = Thermoplastic
Shot style = Standard (A)
Cost/lb = $2.00
Regrind allowed = 50%
Shot weight = [(4 x 20 g) + (80 g)] x 0.5 = 80 g
Part weight = 80 g/4 = 20 g/part, or 4.4 lb/1000 parts
Material cost = $2.00 x 4.4 = $8.8/1000 parts, or $0.088/part

Scenario C

Material = Thermoplastic
Shot style = Runnerless (B)
Cost/lb = $2.00
Regrind allowed = None
Shot weight = 4 x 20 g = 80 g
Part weight = 80 g/4 = 20 g/part, or 4.4 lb/1000 parts
Material cost = $2.00 x 4.4 = $8.8/1000 parts, or $0.088/part

Scenario D

Material = Thermoplastic
Shot style = Runnerless (B)
Cost/lb = $2.00

Regrind allowed = 50% (Assume that regrind is available from another source *i.e.*, an adjacent process)

Shot weight = (4 x 10 g) x 0.5 = 40 g

Part weight = 40 g/4 = 10 g/part, or 2.2 lb/1000 parts

Material cost = $2.00 x 2.2 = $4.4/1000 parts, or $0.044/part

Scenario E

Material = Thermoset

Shot style = Standard (B)

Cost/lb = $0.70

Regrind allowed: None, Thermoset! (Thermosetting plastics cannot be remolded)

Shot weight = (4 x 20 g) + (80 g) = 160 g

Part weight = 160 g/4 = 40 g/part, or 8.8 lb/1000 parts

Material cost = $0.70 x 8.8 = $6.16/1000 parts, or $0.062/part

Regrind is thermoplastic material that was previously molded and for some reason is not usable as good product. This plastic can be granulated and reintroduced into the process at a specified level.

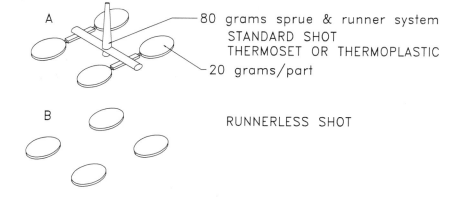

Fig. 4-3 Cost impact of nonproductive material

The material costs decrease with the reduction of nonproductive material and an increase in regrind allowed, whereas labor-related benefits are associated with the elimination of nonproductive material. These labor-related benefits include:

- Reduced material handling, *i.e.*, less plastic material required
- Elimination of part separation from runners, etc.

- Reduction in regrind generation, *i.e.*, less regrind, less risk of material degradation/contamination
- Reduced equipment wear, *i.e.*, less material is processed, little or no material is granulated, and there is less risk of metal contamination from granulator

The pricing of plastic parts manufactured using other processes is similar in that the relative value of nonproductive material is minimized whenever possible. Examples of nonproductive material for thermoforming and blow molding are illustrated in Chapter 3, Fig. 3-19. Extrusion waste should be confined to start-up and shut-down material only.

Plastic Product Recycling

The environmental impact of a product during manufacturing, use, and after it has been discarded needs to be considered during the design process.

When it comes to waste and environmental issues, plastics are singularly the most visible of all the materials. This is not because plastics are the largest volume material discarded, nor is it that plastics cannot be recycled. The reason plastics are the most visible material is that there are few aggressive recycling efforts for plastics. There has been little economic incentive to recycle plastics. It is also difficult to differentiate and identify one plastic from another

Plastics are a growing component of U.S. municipal solid waste

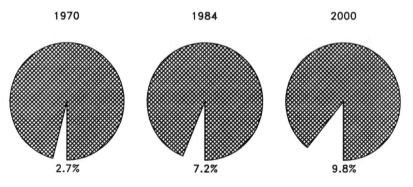

1970	1984	2000
2.7%	7.2%	9.8%

Total waste = 109.9 million tons   Total waste = 133 million tons   Total waste = 158.8 million tons
Total waste values include post-consumer waste and smaller volumes of commercial and industrial discards

Fig. 4-4 Plastics in U.S. landfills. Source: Franklin Associates Ltd., Prairie Village, KS, reprinted from "Waste Solutions," *Modern Plastics Magazine*, McGraw Hill Publishing Co., New York, April 1990

and even more difficult to separate products manufactured with different plastics.

Table 4-2 puts the consumer waste level into perspective. On the other hand the recycling thrusts (see Table 4-3) are an opportunity not yet realized.

Need to Recycle

The moral and ethical need to recycle has always been the banner that is waved in attempts to heighten awareness and increase recycling of all materials. The need to recycle is valid not only from a moral and ethical standpoint, but also from an economical and practical position.

Table 4-2 Reclaiming Plastic from Consumer Waste

Material	Annual discards million ton	Consumer waste recovery, million ton	Recovery rate,%
Aluminum..................	2.1	0.6	28.6
Paper and paperboard ..	62.3	12.9	20.7
Glass..........................	13.9	1.0	7.2
Rubber and leather	3.4	0.1	3.0
Iron and steel	11.3	0.3	2.7
Plastics.......................	9.7	0.1	1.0
Total...........................	100.6	14.4	14.3

Source: Franklin Associates Ltd., Prairie Village, KS, reprinted from "Waste Solutions," *Modern Plastics Magazine*, McGraw-Hill Publishing Co., New York, April 1990.

Table 4-3 Recycling Growth Estimate

	1989 %	1989 Million tons	1994 %	1994 Million tons	Average annual growth rate%
Glass.................	20	0.75	40	1.7	17.8
Metal	19.5	2.6	25.9	4	9
Paper	25	12	28.7	15.4	5.1
Paperboard	32.3	11	37.7	13.2	3.6
Plastics	5	0.1	13	0.4	31

Source: Business Communications Co., Norwalk, CT, reprinted from "Waste Solutions," *Modern Plastics Magazine*,McGraw-Hill Publishing Co., New York, April 1990.

The volume of discarded materials in the United States alone is staggering. Landfills are filling up and closing, and new landfills are not being created quickly enough to absorb the solid waste. Figure 4-4 highlights the proportions of plastic in the U.S. landfills. Common sense suggests that the solution to the solid waste disposal problem is to not have the solid waste in the first place.

How Plastics Degrade

Plastics will eventually degrade, but at a slow rate, maybe after 5 to 5000 years. Even plastics that degrade in a relatively short period of time require air, sunlight, and moisture to facilitate the degradation process. Most solid waste in landfills lies below the surface of earth, and this waste is not exposed to air or sunlight. The bottom line is that even biodegradable plastics do not degrade.

From an examination of other degradable materials in the solid waste stream, it becomes apparent that waste degradation may, in fact, be detrimental to the environment if the degraded components find themselves in the water supplies further down the environmental degradation chain.

Money and Morals

One of the more successful recycling efforts in the United States is in aluminum beverage cans. A quick look at this success story reveals what is required for plastics recycling.

- Aluminum cans are easily identifiable; not only is "Please Recycle" written on the can, but the consumer simply has to squeeze the thin can to identify it.
- Successful recycling of aluminum cans occurs in areas where there is a deposit and refund. The economics of the deposit can be appreciated when reviewing the percentage of aluminum cans recycled in areas that offer no deposit/refund versus areas that have a $0.10 per can deposit/refund.
- Bulk separation of aluminum cans is also relatively easy since the only similar product is the steel can, which can be magnetically separated.

Can All Plastics be Recycled?

Yes, all plastics can be recycled; however, all plastics cannot be remolded or reused in the same type of application as the original product. Those plastics that cannot be remelted can always be granulated and used as filler materials in other plastic, asphalt, or concrete. Plastic reusability is only limited by the imagination.

Why Aren't More Plastics Recycled?

More plastic is not recycled because recycling has not been made economically attractive, both from an individual and corporate standpoint.

A Hypothetical Example. Foam food containers are an eyesore, and they are filling the landfills. Efforts to have consumers separate the foam products and recycle them have met with little success. If a $0.01 deposit/container were added, it would have limited success. Even a $0.05 deposit could result in marginal returns. However, (to exaggerate) if there were a $0.25 deposit on each container, people would not only return them all, but every 10-12 year old would be scouring the streets to collect them!

Once the solution to having plastics returned is achieved, the next step will be to separate one plastic from another. This challenge is being met in the early stages by the use of container codes (see Fig. 4-5), but plastic waste is made up of more than containers. The plastics industry is studying the use of barcoding similar to that used at the grocery store checkout. This barcode will give the product an identifying code that will allow downstream separation equipment to differentiate one material from another.

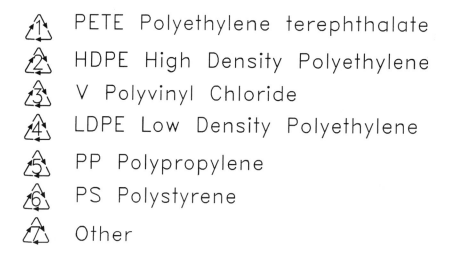

Fig. 4-5 Plastic container material codes

Once the plastic is returned and categorized, its reuse becomes a much simpler matter. The low-cost, reprocessed material will then be economically attractive to processors.

These guidelines to improve the utilization of plastics and reduce plastic waste should be considered in the original design process:

- **Design for maximum functionality.** Reduce and/or combine parts into one product.
- **Design for minimal material use.** Use the least amount of plastic necessary to make the product successful. This includes the product design and the design of the molds/tooling used to manufacture the product.
- **Identify the plastic(s) used to manufacture the product.** Let it be clearly understood by markings and codes.
- **Plan for the product's end-of-life disposal.** Design for a long life cycle, unless the application demands otherwise, and consider how the product may be reused or disposed.
- **Consider using recycled plastic.** If the product cannot be made out of recycled plastic, consider reasonable percentages of regrind to be used.

The plastics product designer plays an important role in determining the environmental impact of plastic parts. This is a tremendous responsibility, but the opportunity exists to design and manufacture plastic products in a conscientious manner to minimize any negative effects on the environment.

Some plastic recycling facts include:

- Plastics accounted for 7.3 wt.% of landfill solid waste in 1986.
- Plastics accounted for 18 vol.% of landfill solid waste in 1986.
- Polystyrene foam accounts for 0.25 wt.% of soild waste.
- 23%, or 170 million pounds, of plastic soft drink containers were recycled in 1988.
- 93 million pounds of milk, juice, and water containers were recycled in 1988.
- The demand for consumer waste recycled HDPE currently exceeds supply.
- Plastic packaging is the most energy efficient packaging to manufacture and transport.

5

Selecting Plastic Materials

Selecting the appropriate plastic material for a specific plastic product/application is one of the most critical steps in the entire design process.

The process of plastic materials selection is further complicated by the fact that there are hundreds of plastic materials manufacturers and thousands of plastic compounds from which the designer can choose.

A Typical Pitfall. Many plastic part designers and processors limit themselves in terms of the variety of plastics in their product portfolios. Many times it is easier to manage a smaller group of materials than to develop a wide material base. Often product designs are forced to fit within a limited material selection range, which could possibly compromise the ultimate product design and performance.

Plastic Material Nomenclature

The first step in understanding how to select plastic materials is learning the language of plastics. Chapter 2 introduced the basic terminology of plastics from the perspective of the polymer, but designers, suppliers, processors, and customers have a different vernacular.

Plastic Material Classification

Starting with the broadest category of plastic classification, the designer determines the type of plastic required.

Thermoplastic: Solidifies upon cooling, and materials can be reprocessed, or are reversible

Thermoset: Sets upon heating, and materials cannot be reprocessed, or are irreversible

The next classification levels focus only on thermoplastic materials since the majority of plastic compounds are thermoplastic. These classifications may vary and overlap depending on the specific plastic compound identified (see Table 5-1).

Commodity: The most widely used plastic materials and they are often the lowest-cost plastics.

Transitional: Plastics that have a broad cost and performance range and overlap into both the commodity and engineering classification. Most common molding grade thermosetting plastics, *i.e.*, phenolic, melamine, epoxy, and alkyd (polyester), would also be considered transitional materials.

Engineering: Plastics used for their performance characteristics and are often reinforced with glass. Engineering plastics are frequently used as alternatives for wood, metal, and glass.

Performance or Advanced: Plastics often developed for aerospace or electronic applications and environments where engineering materials would be marginal or fail. Performance plastics are slow to enter into the common end-use market applications because costs are initially prohibitive; however, costs drop dramatically as applications increase.

Plastic Material Trends

Figure 5-1 illustrates the growth and maturation of a variety of materials relative to the Gross National Product (GNP). Engineering and advanced (performance) plastics will experience the largest growth over the next 10 to 20 years.

Plastic Material Suppliers

The plastic material supplier is the prime resource for identifying plastic materials for specific applications. The number of suppliers of plastic materials (see Fig. 5-2) can be overwhelming, especially when one is trying to compare similar materials from two or more different suppliers. It is critical that the individual selecting the plastic material for a product understand material names, properties, and similarities.

Table 5-1 Classification of Thermoplastic Polymers

	Commodity	Transitional	Engineering	Performance,
	Polyethylene	ABS/SAN	Modified PPO/PPE	Fluoropolymers
	Polypropylene	Acrylics	Nylon (6 and 66)	Liquid crystal polymers (a)
	Polystyrene	SMA copolymer (a)	PBT	Nylon 11 and 12
	Polyvinyl chloride	Glass-filled PP (a)	PET (glass-filled) (a)	Polyamideimide
	PET (bottle grade)	Glass-filled PE (a)	Polyacetal	Polyarylate
			Polycarbonate	Polyetheretherketone
			Alloys and blends (a)	Polyetherimide
			SMA terpolymer (a)	Polyethersulfone
				Polyimide
				Polyphenylene sulfide
				Polysulfone
Volume in pounds ..	1 billion or more	500 million to 1 billion	100 to 500 million	Less than 20 million
Processability	High	Good	Good	Least
Thermal stability....	Low	Medium	High	Excellent
Chemistry/process .	Simple	Intermediate	Intermediate	Complex
Price per pound...... (1986) $/lb	0.25 to 0.75	0.75 to 1.25	1.25 to 3.00	3.00 to 20.00
Growth rate .... %		2 to 5	2 to 6	5 to 8

(a) Developing. Source: "Plastics A.D. 2000," Society of the Plastics Industry, Washington, DC.

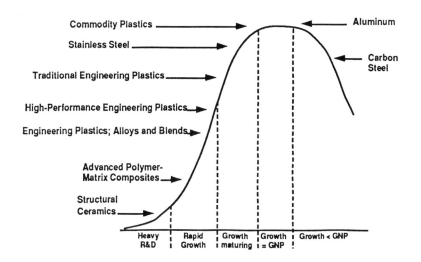

Fig. 5-1 Materials growth relative to the GNP. Source: *ASM News*, ASM International, Metals Park, OH, December, 1989.

Some plastic suppliers are in a better position to support the materials selection process than others. Plastic material suppliers can be classified into five major groups.

Material manufacturers: Manufacturers usually have the best technical support since they manufacture and compound the materials they sell. Technical support from material manufacturers, however, is biased toward the materials they manufacture.

Material compounders: Compounders purchase neat plastic, *i.e.,* polymer with little or no additives, and they specialize in customizing the plastic by adding reinforcements and property modifiers to meet a narrower market than that served by the material manufacturer. The technical support from a compounder begins with their compounding efforts.

Material distributors: Material distributors are marketing a needed service to both the large and small plastics users. Basically, the distributor develops a materials network with several material manufacturers and provides a single source for a wide range of plastics. Distributors offer virtually all the services of the manufacturer. Many distributors are, in fact, controlled by material manufacturers. In some cases the portfolio of plastics offered by distributors may be limited to those materials that are not in direct competition with the products of the owning manufacturer.

Material brokers: Material brokers offer limited technical resources. The broker keeps a "pulse" on the surplus plastic market and sells materials as they become available. Batch variation and product consistency may be

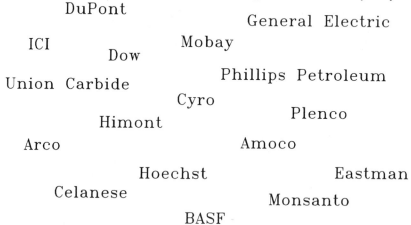

Fig. 5-2 Some key plastic manufacturers

issues of concern with plastics purchased through brokers. However, if the plastic product is robust, *i.e.*, unaffected by possible material and color/ processing variations, the broker's plastic compound will often be priced significantly lower than other market resources.

Material reprocessors: Reprocessors obtain surplus plastic, both virgin and used, from a variety of markets, *i.e.*, excess inventory from material manufacturers, odd color lots from processors, etc. The material is often colored and/or compounded, then repelletized to provide a uniform physical size. The reprocessor offers limited technical support, and the reprocessed plastic may vary in properties beyond acceptable limits for many product applications.

Plastics Nomenclature

What name(s) are used to refer to plastic materials? This area is also very confusing due to the variety of colorful tradenames and nicknames used in the plastics industry.

The vernacular of the plastic industry also varies depending on the area of material use; for example, polypropylene is the name of a commodity plastic. A purchasing agent or engineer may refer to polypropylene as propylene. A molding supervisor may refer to the same material as polypro. The material handler responsible for keeping molding equipment full of plastic may refer to the same material simply as poly, and the material supplier may call polypropylene by a tradename such as Pro-Fax (Himont).

Table 5-2 highlights some of the many ways plastic materials are named. See Appendix A for a more complete listing.

Table 5-2 Typical Plastic Nomenclature

Generic	Polymer	Manufacturer	Acronym	Nickname
Propylene	Polypropylene	Aristech, Rexene	PP	Polypro
Nylon	Polyamide	Zytel (DuPont)	PA	Nylon
ABS...........................	Polyacrylonitrite butadiene styrene	Cycloac (GE) Lustran (Monsanto)	ABS	ABS
Polyester.....................	Polyethylene terephthalate	Rynite (DuPont)	PET	PET
Polyester.....................	Polybutylene terephthalate	Valox (GE)	PBT	PBT
Carbonate	Polycarbonate	Lexan (GE)	PC	Polycarb
Acetal	Polyacetal (polyoxymethylene)	Delrin (DuPont), Celcon (Celanese)	POM	Acetal

Plastic Material Selection Process

Chapter 4 explores how to define specific properties and characteristics of a plastic product. Selecting the appropriate plastic material for a specific application requires that specific properties and characteristics of candidate materials be identified and compared.

To begin this process, designers and engineers must arm themselves with more information about some of the more global characteristics of plastic materials.

Plastics Property References

Where do you find specific property information on plastic materials? See Fig. 5-3. There are four main resources for plastic materials.

Manufacturer's Literature. This is the most thorough source of property data as it relates to a particular manufacturer's plastic(s). Although very thorough, it may have an element of bias when it comes to the property comparison with competitors' plastics.

Encyclopedias and Material Selectors. These are compilations of manufacturers' data. They are mostly duplications of the manufacturer's literature with the exception that they are edited in a standard format that allows comparisons to be made quickly. These data resources may also pro-

Fig. 5-3 Plastic material references

vide property ranges, *i.e.*, low and high values, instead of specific values. The ranges may cloud the material selection process, but they are useful in making a broad judgment on candidate materials.

On-line Databases. This service appeals to many plastic designers and processors because it allows the computer to do the search based on the user's input of desired attributes. The more attributes input, the more refined the search. As an example, if the user desires a certain tensile strength, impact strength, and specific gravity, the on-line database accepts the inputs and begins searching for candidate materials within a specified range or tolerance.

It is important to understand the materials presented in a database may only include the materials offered by a limited amount of material suppliers; therefore, the completeness of the database may be inadequate for a specific application.

Experience. This is the most valuable source of data for any design or processing effort. In many cases experience will exceed the manufacturer's published data. Many design teams work to develop their own databases derived from both good and bad results.

Balancing Properties
The selection of plastic materials for specific product applications requires that the properties be balanced (see Fig. 5-4). Balancing means that the selec-

Optimize Material Selection

▼ Balance products requirements to material properties

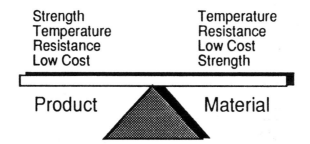

Fig. 5-4 Plastic product design strategy

tion process has considered all the major properties required by the application and all the secondary properties have also been considered.

Some examples of secondary properties would be: ability to be processed, cost, and appearance.

This is an example of what may happen when all the properties are not considered: A study revealed that a new engineering thermoplastic met or exceeded all the major property requirements; however, the cost of the material was $8.75 per pound, making it unacceptable in the marketplace. Further study revealed that the high impact strength was significantly beyond the actual customer requirements. A standard grade engineering material would meet the new balanced properties.

As plastic material properties are understood and the process of comparing different plastics begins, it will be quickly learned that all plastics have an Achilles' Heel, *i.e.*, one or more attributes that may be an inherent weak point in the material. The job of the product designer is to comprehend these material issues and design around them.

Published Properties

The publication of plastic properties, regardless of their source, usually follows a similar format. First there are the overall material attributes:

- Toughness
- Processibility
- Chemical resistance
- Ability to be colored

Although they offer a quick preview of some of the material characteristics, these attributes are inadequate for selecting one plastic over another. The next level of property review involves these categories:

- Physical
- Mechanical
- Thermal
- Electrical
- Chemical
- Regulatory and environmental
- Time related

Physical Properties

Specific gravity is defined as the ratio of the mass of a specified volume of material compared to the mass of the same volume of water. Some manufacturers will report density with the comparable weight per unit volume.

The range for specific gravity values of plastics is wide, as illustrated in Fig. 5-5. See Appendix B for more values. Polypropylene can be as low as 0.9 and glass/mineral-filled thermosets can exceed 2.0.

In addition to specific gravity, most manufacturers will also provide data on specific volume, expressed in cubic inches/ounce or cubic centimeters/gram, to offer the material selector the opportunity to determine exact material content.

Rule of Thumb. To convert specific gravity, or density, to specific volume (lb./in.^{3}), multiply by 0.036. A plastic with a specific gravity of 1.2 will have a specific volume of (1.3 x 0.036) 0.0432 lb./in.^{3}

Specific Gravity Trap

Many designers, purchasers, and processors believe plastics are all the same. The pitfall with this assumption is that different grades or colors of the same plastic family may have slightly different specific gravities.

This scenario clarifies the point: A purchasing agent has been buying a thermoplastic (referred to as Poly A) at a cost of $2.05/lb. in quantities of 250,000 lb./year. Poly A has a specific gravity of 1.15.

Another plastics manufacturer claims that his plastic (referred to as Poly B) will cost only $1.95 for the same quantity. Poly B has a specific gravity of 1.23. On day 1 the purchasing agent is a hero, claiming to have saved the company $0.10 x 250,000 = $25,000. At the end of the year he was fired for costing the company at least $10,000 because he did not consider the increase in specific gravity!

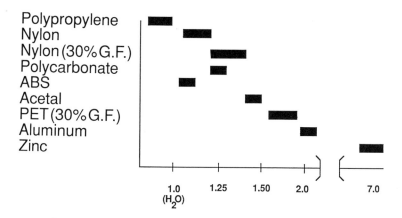

Fig. 5-5 Specific gravity (density) values

Mold Shrinkage. All plastics shrink. Some shrink uniformly in all directions; others shrink at different rates in different directions. The shrinkage is measured as the percent change in the size of the plastic part when compared to the mold. Shrinkage is expressed both as a percentage and as in./in. or mm/mm; 1% shrinkage equals 0.01 in./in. or 0.01 mm/mm.

Rule of Thumb. Amorphous plastics, such as polystyrene, ABS, acrylics, or polycarbonates, tend to be isotropic in behavior, *i.e.*, they have similar property values in all directions when not compounded with reinforcements. See Fig. 5-6 and 5-7.

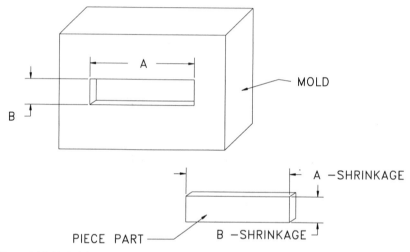

Fig. 5-6 Mold shrinkage

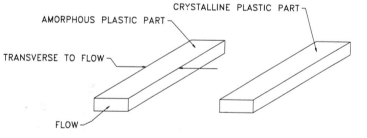

AMORPHOUS SHRINKAGE RATE
FLOW DIRECTION – .006 INCH/INCH
TRANSVERSE DIRECTION – .006 INCH/INCH

CRYSTALLINE SHRINKAGE RATE
FLOW DIRECTION – .015 INCH/INCH
TRANSVERSE DIRECTION – .020 INCH/INCH

Fig. 5-7 Isotropic/anisotropic shrinkage. Plastic is reinforced with glass fibers.

Crystalline plastics, such as polyolefins, nylon, acetals, and thermoplastic polyesters, tend to exhibit a degree of molecular orientation, which results in anisotropic behavior, *i.e.*, different property values in all directions. Anisotropy becomes exaggerated when reinforcements and fillers are added.

A simple way to understand the anisotropic behavior of crystalline plastics is to compare them to wood. A board is easier to cut with the grain than it is to cut across the grain.

The shrinkage of plastic is complex. Most of the shrinkage occurs within the mold; however, most plastic will also exhibit a continuing shrinkage outside of the mold that may continue for days or years. This is referred to as postmold shrinkage (PMS), and for most plastics it is an insignificant value. There are a few plastics , *e.g.*, acetal, that exhibit this phenomenon to a degree where it must be considered in the product design and mold build. See Fig. 5-8.

This basic equation applies to all plastics:

$$TS = MS + PMS$$

where TS=total shrinkage, MS= mold shrinkage, and PMS= postmold shrinkage.

A product should be designed for the total shrinkage value, and every attempt should be made to maximize the mold shrinkage and, therefore, minimize the postmold shrinkage.

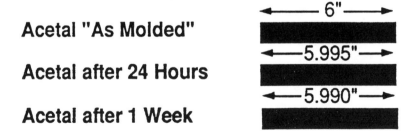

Acetal "As Molded"

Acetal after 24 Hours

Acetal after 1 Week

Total shrinkage = Mold Shrinkage + Post Mold Shrinkage

Fig. 5-8 Postmold shrinkage

Moisture. Many plastics are hygroscopic, which means that they absorb water. Water is an undesirable addition during the processing of plastics. Any moisture present will vaporize at the processing temperatures; this vapor (or steam) will diffuse throughout the plastic melt, resulting in undesirable voids or pockets in the plastic part. Each of these voids will be sites for product failure, perhaps due to lower impact strength or early fatigue failure.

The amount of moisture absorbed by plastic varies from virtually zero to as much as 1%. See Fig. 5-9. The majority of this moisture can be removed by the plastic processor using material dryers and/or vented processing machines. See Chapter 3 for further discussion. The presence of moisture in the plastic resin before processing is relatively easy to determine with basic analyzing equipment; however, moisture in the plastic part after processing is difficult to detect. Therefore, all efforts should be made to detect and remove moisture prior to processing.

Adding moisture to plastic parts is sometimes considered to be desirable especially at times when short-term softening is required. A good example is nylon 6/6, which is one of the most notorious of the hygroscopic plastic materials. A product that is made of nylon 6/6 may be a cap or cover that is

Plastics and Water

Many plastics can absorb water
  (Hygroscopic) from 0.1% to 1%
Water changes properties (softens plastic)

—Water Absorption—

Plastics That Do	Plastics That Do Not
Nylon	Polystyrene
Polyesters	Polypropylene
Polycabonate	Polyethylene
ABS	

Fig. 5-9 Moisture absorbed by plastic

pressed over a metal rod. The press fit of the nylon over the rod may be facilitated by exposing the part to steam, which will be absorbed by the nylon and act as a plasticizer, temporarily softening the part and making assembly easier. Over time and dry conditions, the nylon part will lose some of the absorbed moisture and return to a rigid or brittle condition.

Cost is often overlooked. As mentioned earlier, the classic cost consideration of price/pound is inadequate for proper design application. Today's manufacturing environment emphasizes material and product value as opposed to material cost.

More expensive plastics may offer cost-reduction benefits later in the manufacturing process that could significantly outweigh the additional expense of the plastic itself.

Plastic material selection must involve consideration of these important factors:

- Cost to manufacture
- Cost to assemble
- Durability, *i.e.*, cost of returned product
- Packaging
- Disposal costs, both to the manufacturer and to the consumer

A good example would be the conversion of a bracket from steel to plastic. The steel in the old bracket may cost a total of $0.50 while the total cost of the plastic may be $1.50. The $1.00 per bracket material cost increase could easily be justified when the "downstream" manufacturing costs of machining and coating the metal are compared to the molding of a plastic bracket that is ready to use.

The relative cost of some plastics is illustrated in Fig. 5-10.

Mechanical Properties

Product designers who have years of experience designing with metal are quick to note the uniqueness of plastics and their mechanical behavior. Many plastics, because of their viscoelastic nature, pass through a yield stage before experiencing complete failure. Refer to Chapter 2, Fig. 2-10.

Tensile Properties. The tensile properties are often the first mechanical properties compared when selecting a plastic. See Fig. 5-11.

Tensile properties such as tensile strength, elastic modulus, yield stress, ultimate stress, and toughness are derived by "pulling" a test specimen at a predetermined rate and measuring the force and deformation, or stretch, of the

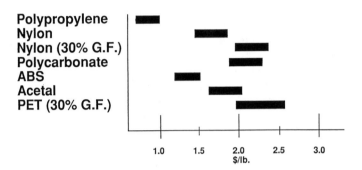

Fig. 5-10 Relative cost of plastics

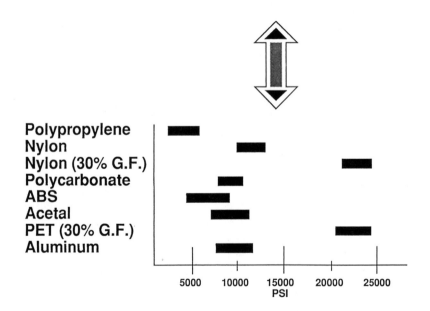

Fig. 5-11 Tensile strength

specimen. Two basic definitions need to be understood when discussing tensile properties (see Fig. 5-12):

Stress: The force applied divided by the cross-sectional area. Expressed in units of psi or Pa

Strain: The deformation that results from the applied stress. Measured as the change in length divided by the original length; it is either unitless or expressed in units of in./in. or mm/mm

The tensile strength for plastics can be either: (1) measured at the yield point on the stress-strain curve (called tensile strength at yield or the yield stress); or (2) measured when the specimen breaks (called tensile strength at break). The higher of these two tensile strengths is also referred to as the ultimate tensile strength (see Fig. 5-13).

Comparing these values also requires two key assumptions:

1. All values compared were measured at the same temperature.
2. The test method was the same; ASTM standard D638 describes the most common test.

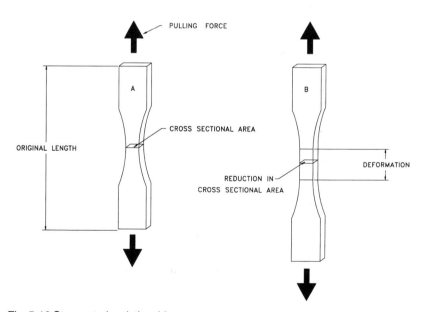

Fig. 5-12 Stress-strain relationship

Elastic Modulus. This is the slope of the initial or linear portion of the stress-strain curve (Fig. 5-13) and is often referred to as Young's modulus. The units of modulus are psi or Pa.

Elongation. Most plastics have some degree of elasticity, which is characterized by the linear or straight line portion of the stress-strain curve. The elongation is the amount of strain a plastic material can be subjected to so that when the load is removed, the plastic will return to its original length without any permanent deformation.

Elastomers are those plastics that can be stretched to at least 2 times their original length without experiencing a permanent deformation.

Toughness, often thought of as a qualitative term, can be calculated by measuring the area under the stress-strain curve (see Fig. 5-14) and can be expressed as unit of energy per unit volume, or J/m.

Impact strength has clearly become one of the differentiating characteristics of plastic materials. Impact strength, although similar to toughness, should not be considered the same as toughness. Impact strength assumes that there is a sudden and rapid loading as opposed to the relatively slow loading of a tensile-type test.

The sudden loading is developed by the impact tester, shown in Fig. 5-15, which has a hammer that swings and strikes a mounted specimen. The energy lost (the hammer swing is less after it strikes the specimen) is assumed to be absorbed by the plastic specimen. The more energy absorbed by the plastic,

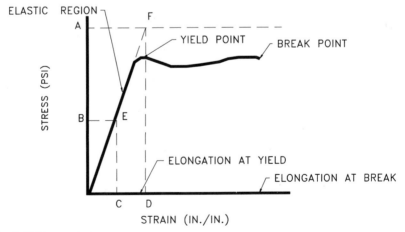

Fig. 5-13 Stress-strain curve

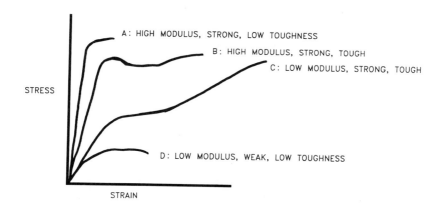

Fig. 5-14 Modulus, strength, and toughness

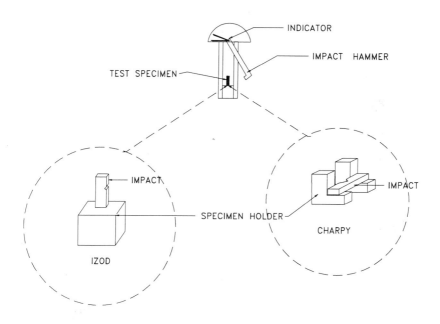

Fig. 5-15 Impact tester

the greater the impact strength value. Impact strength is measured in units of in.-lb. or J/m.

Since plastic materials exhibit a wide range of impact properties, many impact test variations have been devised. Again, care has to be taken to ensure that materials are being compared using the same test method.

Many plastics exhibit impact "notch sensitivity," which means that some plastics that display superior impact properties may lose their superior impact value when a notch is cut into the specimen. This phenomenon has resulted in the notched impact test. There are two popular impact tests:

- **Izod:** The test specimen is notched and mounted vertically holding only one end. The impact hammer strikes the top of the specimen on the side with the notch (Fig. 5-15).
- **Charpy:** This test is common throughout Europe and is similar to the Izod with the exception that the test specimen is held horizontally and supported on both ends (Fig. 5-15)

One of the overlooked impact characteristics of some plastics is "critical thickness." Basically stated, critical thickness is when the impact strength of a plastic decreases as the wall thickness of the plastic part increases. See Fig. 5-16.

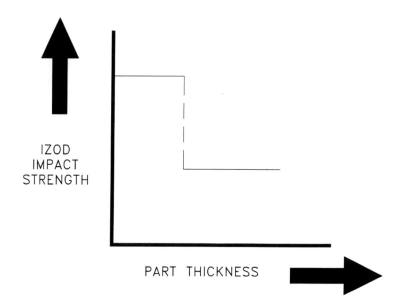

IZOD
IMPACT
STRENGTH

PART THICKNESS

Fig. 5-16 Impact strength and critical thickness

The failure mode goes from the high-impact absorbing ductile failure to a low-impact absorbing brittle failure.

For many metal designers this phenomenon is the opposite of the behavior commonly seen in nonplastics.

Flexural strength is the stress (force/area) required to bend a supported beam (Fig. 5-17); the stiffer the plastic, the greater the flexural values. As with tensile strength and tensile modulus, there is a value for both flexural strength and flexural modulus.

Temperature and Plastics

Plastics are excellent thermal insulators. They do not transfer heat well, and if properly coated, they can even be made to reflect heat. This thermal insulating characteristic is the reason that materials such as polyester bats, foamed styrene, urethane, and aluminized mylar film are used for insulating clothing, sleeping bags, coffee cups, and thermal blankets.

Flammability. Plastics burn. The important questions to ask when comparing the flammability of different plastics are:

- How easily is the plastic ignited?
- How quickly does the plastic burn?
- How much thermal enegy does the plastic possess?
- Are there any smoke or toxic fumes generated when the plastic burns?

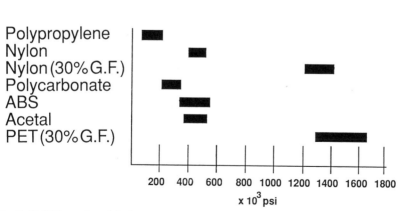

Fig. 5-17 Stiffness (modulus)

The test results commonly used in comparing plastics and flammability were derived from the Underwriters Laboratory (UL) and adapted by ASTM. There are two basic tests for classifying plastics flammability.

Horizontal burning test (94 HB). Materials are classified 94 HB if they burn over a 3-in. span in a horizontal bar test not more than 1.5 in./min. for specimens between 0.120 and 0.500 in. thick and not more then 3 in./min. for specimens less than 0.120 in. thick.

Vertical burning test (94 V-0, 94 V-1, 94 V-2). The vertical test is more stringent than the horizontal test, and 94 V-0 is a more stringent rating than the HB series. The criteria for rating vertical tests include multiple ignition attempts and rate of burn.

It is possible to improve the flammability rating of a plastic with the addition of flame retardants. These additives may also have some side-effects such as lower mechanical properties that must be considered.

Toxicity. As plastic burns, fumes may be given off depending on the chemical composition of the plastic and its additives. Burned polyethylene smells like candle wax; polystyrene burns with a black soot evolved from the benzene content. Other plastics may yield fumes that irritate or are toxic. One of the best ways to compare burning by-products is to review their material safety data sheets (MSDS). These sheets are available from all plastic manufacturers; they provide information about burning by-products, health issues, and disposal requirements.

Most plastic properties vary with changes in temperature

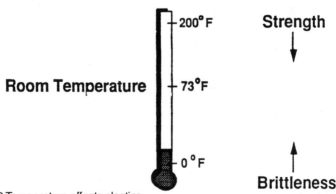

Fig. 5-18 Temperature affects plastics

Hot and Cold Temperatures

Most thermoplastic materials become stiffer when temperature is lowered and somewhat weaker when temperature is increased. Each plastic compound behaves differently at different temperatures, but the majority of plastic applications will work well between 32 and 150 °F with the assumption of no mechanical loading. As the environment begins to exceed this range, many plastic material performance characteristics change. See Fig. 5-18.

There are plastic materials that work well at temperatures over 500 °F and below –100 °F, but these are exceptions.

The Temperature Pitfall. The selection of plastic materials relative to the temperatures that will be experienced by the product should always be expanded to consider what environments will be encountered in shipping, storage, and common customer use. Initial material selection for a typical electronic calculator or computer housing may be based on the average temperature of an office, *i.e.*, 60 to 80 °F. Imagine the surprise when the manufacturer learns that the back of the truck that ships his product from New York to Arizona exceeds 140 °F or that the consumer is a student who likes to throw the calculator on the dash of his car for a week when left in the sun with the temperature rising over 150 °F.

The total temperature exposure possibilities need to be considered.

Thermal Expansion

Plastics have a higher thermal expansion (expressed in in./in./°F or mm/mm/°C) than most other materials. This fact needs to be considered carefully, especially when designing plastic assemblies that include plastic parts tightly fastened to dissimilar materials, such as plastic to metal, or when attaching two different plastics. See Fig. 5-19.

Metal fasteners are commonly used with plastic. A plastic may expand at a rate 2 to 8 times greater than the metal. This means that a metal insert that was press fit into a plastic assembly at room temperature may pull out when the assembly experiences a temperature over 200 °F.

A good example of plastic expansion can also be seen in vinyl siding for houses. The vinyl siding is extruded and cut into long continuous profiles. The siding is attached to the house loosely by tacking nails that are in slots versus holes in the vinyl profile. This allows the long plastic siding profiles to expand and contract as the temperature changes. If the vinyl siding were rigidly nailed to the house, the siding would buckle and crack. The designer who requires thermal properties must consider these factors, and design criteria and/or material selection must compensate for these thermal properties.

Plastics expand more than metal

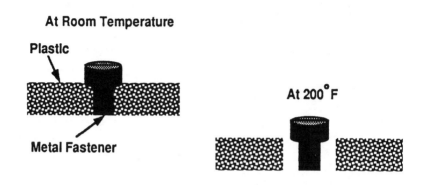

Fig. 5-19 Plastics and thermal expansion

Expansion of plastics should be considered, especially when designing circular products such as gears, bushings, and bearings. In these instances, the outside temperature is not as much a factor as the thermal changes associated with frictional heat. Improper expansion calculations will result in seizing of plastic bearings about a rotating shaft.

Deformation Under Load (ASTM D648). Sometimes referred to as DTUL or heat deflection temperature (HDT) in the product property literature, it describes the phenomenon of plastic deforming under a constant load when exposed to an increase in temperature.

The test for HDT in plastics is to place a test specimen (5 in. x 1/2 in. x 1/4 in.) in a thermal bath (heat transfer oil) and increase the temperature at a constant rate (2 °C/minute). The specimen is loaded at either 66 or 264 psi (see Fig. 5-20). The temperature at which a deflection of 0.010 in. is observed is the HDT value.

Most thermal properties for plastics are variations of this test. As with any selection process, care has to be taken to be sure that the values comparing different plastics are from the same test method. This is especially important in the area of thermal tests where many tests sound the same, but are conducted under different conditions.

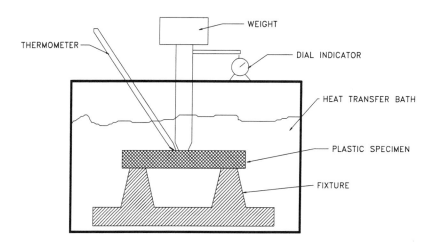

THERMOMETER

WEIGHT

DIAL INDICATOR

HEAT TRANSFER BATH

PLASTIC SPECIMEN

FIXTURE

Fig. 5-20 Heat deflection temperature test

Electrical Properties

The earliest applications for plastics were in the electrical markets because plastics are excellent dielectrics (electrical insulators). This insulating quality occurs because plastics hold their outer electrons tightly (as opposed to metals, which have free electrons and give them up easily).

Comparing the relative electrical insulating abilities of plastics requires some unique standardized tests: volume resistivity, dielectric strength, and arc resistance.

Volume Resistivity (ASTM D257). Volume resistivity is the ability of a material to impede or resist the flow of DC current through the thickness of a test specimen, usually a 1-cm cube (see Fig. 5-21). The units are ohm-cm. Materials with volume resistivities greater than 10^8 ohm-cm are considered good electrical insulators.

Dielectric Strength (ASTM D149). Dielectric strength is the ratio of the breakdown voltage to the thickness of the material. The breakdown voltage is the voltage that the plastic can withstand before electrical breakdown occurs. The units are volts/mil (a mil is 0.001 in.). To conduct the dielectric strength test AC current is passed through the test specimen; the voltage is increased at a specified rate. Eventually the plastic will break down resulting in conduction; this point is the dielectric strength.

Dielectric strength is important in the insulation of wire and cable, printed circuits, and the encapsulation of electrical products.

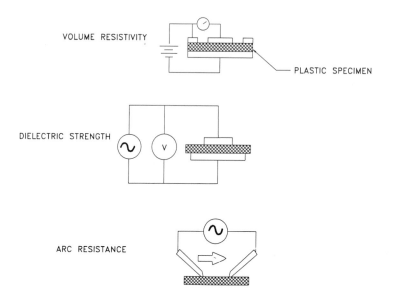

Fig. 5-21 Electrical tests

Arc Resistance, (ASTM D149). Arc resistance determines the amount of time elapsed before the surface of a plastic material breaks down and forms a conductive path.

The results of this test are useful in electrical applications such as switches, contactors, and other devices that tend to generate a spark or electrical arc during normal use.

When plastic materials are exposed to an electric arc, the surface of the organic polymer carbonizes. This carbon is conductive and allows the arc and the carbon track to propagate.

Additives and modifiers could adversely affect electrical properties and lower arc resistance values if they are inherently incompatible with the plastic.

The arc resistance test (Fig. 5-21) is conducted using a plastic test specimen and two electrodes spaced a fixed distance (0.635 cm) apart. They are energized with a high voltage and low current. The time required to form a conductive path is the arc resistance, which is measured in seconds.

Chemical Resistance

There are several standard tests for comparing the chemical resistance of plastic materials, but the important issues associated with chemical resistance relate directly to how the plastic is going to be used in the product application. For example, plastic for an automotive application will need to resist solvents, gasoline, and oils, whereas plastic for a 2-liter pop bottle will need to resist mild acids and water.

Considering all the possible chemicals is important. Too often common chemicals such as soap, water, milk, and alcohol are overlooked. Also, gases and the resistance to the penetration of gases should be considered. For example, high density polyethylene (milk jug plastic) could not be used for 2-liter pop bottles because it breathes allowing the carbon dioxide fizz to escape.

Crazing. The result of chemical attack on plastic varies from dissolution to discoloration. One attack format is crazing, which is a slow degradation that begins with slight discoloration, followed by the formation of a multitude of hairline fractures; it ultimately leads to total mechanical failure. Crazing occurs when a solvent such as methylene chloride or acetone comes in contact with plastics such as acrylic, polystyrene, or polycarbonate.

Regulatory and Environmental Issues. Regulatory and environmental aspects of materials are of global concern. Independent confirmation of plastic material properties and product application/design is required in most electrical and consumer-oriented products. Underwriters' Laboratories (UL) and Engineering Testing Laboratory (ETL) are two agencies used in the United States. However, the globalization of markets demands that the plastic product designer be aware that there are similar agencies in each country from which approval must be secured.

Other agencies, such as the Food and Drug Administration (FDA), the Environmental Protection Agency (EPA), and the Occupational Safety and Health Administration (OSHA), may have to be contacted when plastic materials and products are in contact with food items or the waste stream. As mentioned earlier, the material safety data sheet (MSDS) is an excellent starting point for understanding these issues and how they relate to a specific plastic in for a particular application.

Time-Related Properties

Most plastic materials are selected based on their short-term properties. This may be adequate in the initial material selection process, but there is still a need to understand how a material will behave over a long period of time, specifically the expected life of the product.

Typical time-related properties are:

- Creep
- Stress relaxation
- Fatigue endurance

Creep is the permanent deformation of a plastic over time, and under a constant load, and at a constant temperature. The important factor is time. See Fig. 5-22.

A product designer may select a plastic based on its modulus E (E = stress/strain), but may learn that the phenomenon of creep resulted in an early product failure. The strain or deformation caused by creep can be determined from the manufacturer's data and the modulus equation can be modified so that E represents the apparent modulus (E = stress/strain + strain associated with creep. This apparent modulus provides the designer with a more realistic value for designing products for a long life.

Plastics may continue to stretch under a constant load (creep)

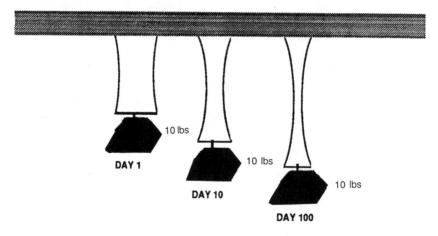

Fig. 5-22 Plastics and creep

Stress Relaxation. Stress relaxation is the decreasing stress required to effect a constant strain at a constant temperature. The chemical mechanism that causes a plastic to undergo creep also applies to the phenomenon of stress relaxation. In fact, many designers employ the same apparent modulus used in creep for stress relaxation.

A good way to understand stress relaxation is through examples of products: A gasket in a jar may exhibit stress relaxation over time and have to be retightened. A snap fit that holds two plastic parts together tightly when originally assembled may prove to be loose over time. A self-tapping screw mounted in a plastic part may loosen over time due to stress relaxation. As with creep, the plastic product designer will need to consider stress relaxation to ensure proper performance over the product's life.

Fatigue endurance of plastics and plastic parts is measured by applying and removing specified loads at a specified cycle. The number of cycles prior to failure is the most common measure of fatigue endurance. The designer has to be aware that fatigue endurance tests and measurements are varied and that specific product testing, as opposed to laboratory specimen tests, is the best way to determine endurance.

The need to understand fatigue endurance can be seen in the example of a product that was loaded into the trailer of a truck and shipped across the country on the interstate highway system. Although the ride appeared to be smooth and steady, there will always be a degree of low-level vibration in such conditions. The journey turned out to be an unwanted five-day cycle loading test that resulted in the fatigue failure of the product!

Fatigue endurance should always be a plastic part design consideration in applications where motors and transportation vehicles are present.

Material Matrix

How do you assemble all the data and make a logical decision as to which plastic to select? The material matrix is an excellent tool for the material selector to use for both compiling and analyzing a variety of different plastics.

The material selection process involves these steps:
1. Define your product needs.
2. Define your process and tooling objectives.
3. Select several candidate materials.
4. Develop a material matrix.
5. Match product needs to plastic properties.
6. Make plastic selection(s).
7. Explore candidate material(s) in more detail.

What basic properties do you require? As discussed in Chapter 4, key product attributes need to be outlined before the material selection process can begin. The necessary attributes may be mechanical, electrical, or chemical properties.

Does your product have any special requirements? Product features such as snap fits, mounting, coating (printing/plating/painting), bonding, welding, and assembly may put unique demands on the plastic material to be selected.

Are there any environmental concerns? What temperature demands (high and low) will the product require? Will there be a need to have electromagnetic interference (EMI) shielding? How will the presence of moisture affect the product? Are there any health issues with humans, animals, or plants?

What are the time-related requirements? Will the product experience any cyclical loading, long exposure to the outdoors (ultraviolet radiation), or constant loads?

How will the product/material be processed? Consideration of the process may shed light on the material candidate. Will the product be thermoformed, injection molded, extruded, etc.? See Chapter 3.

Are there any special tooling requirements? Will the material selected and the product design require new or modified tools? Has the product been designed for automation and assembly?

As these questions are answered, the individual doing the material selection can start to eliminate the materials that do not meet the requirements, that are too expensive, that cannot be processed as required, or that do not meet tooling requirements.

The material selector must not assume that the plastic to be selected using the matrix will be obvious. Such an assumption will only narrow the plastic portfolio. All marginal plastic candidates should be considered along with the obvious plastic candidates.

The matrix can be as simple or as extensive as the material selector determines. Obviously, if more data are compared, the resolution of the matrix will be better.

Matrix Construction

The matrix is a simple grid with the desired attributes listed vertically on the left margin and the candidate materials listed across the top. See Fig. 5-23.

Each material is assessed as to the relative value for each attribute. As an example, if three plastics are being considered for good impact strength, the plastics can be ranked. The plastic with the highest impact strength would be given a 5, the middle material a 3, and the plastic with the lowest impact strength a 1. The actual attribute values are not used in the matrix, but should be logged for later reference. If listed attributes are not considered of equal weight, they can be ranked and weighed.

As an example, a product design for a toy may have an attribute list like this:

Attribute	Rank	Weight
Density	3	1
Impact Strength	1	5
Flammability	2	3

As the material candidate properties are ranked, their rank number is multiplied by the weight factor for that particular property value. This will result in a clearer definition of the type of plastic required for the application.

After all the ranking and weighing is completed, the total and average for each plastic candidate is calculated. The material with the highest average is a prime candidate for this application.

Material Matrix Exercise

Consider the application of plastic siding for the housing market. The plastic to be selected must be durable, colorable, and relatively inexpensive. The initial list of material candidates consists of:

- ABS
- Rigid PVC
- Polycarbonate (PC)
- High density polyethylene (HDPE)

The literature search for specific property values resulted in the following data:

	ABS	PC	HDPE	PVC
Density	1.04	1.2	0.96	1.35
HDT(66)	200 °F	280 °F	185 °F	150 °F
Chemical Resistivity	Low	Low	High	Low
94 V-0	No	Yes	No	Yes
Cyclic Loading	Low	High	Medium	Medium
CTE (x 10^{-6}in./in.)	90	68	90	85
Flexural Modulus (x 10^3)	220	340	190	350
Colorability	Poor	Excellent	Good	Excellent
U.V. Stability	Excellent	Poor	Good	Excellent

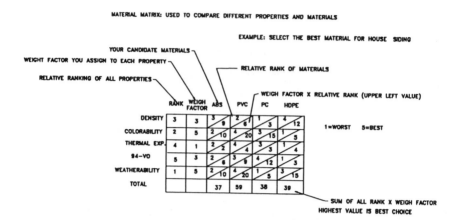

Fig. 5-23 Material selection matrix

Factoring the property values into the matrix is illustrated in Fig. 5-23. The value in the upper left corner represents the relative rank of each of the listed plastics for that specific property. The value in the lower right is the product of the weight factor and the materials rank. This weighted value is then summed and averaged.

Based on the results of this exercise, PVC would be considered the best material for this application. The material matrix should, of course, be expanded to include more properties and more candidate plastics to provide a more thorough survey.

6

Wall of a Plastic Part

The wall of a plastic part has to perform many functions ranging from allowing the plastic melt an opportunity to flow during processing to providing an exterior surface that satisfies the customer's requirements in terms of appearance.

For products designed using metal or wood, it can be assumed that the structural integrity of the product is a function of the material selected; however, when a product is designed and manufactured with plastic, nothing can be assumed. Structural integrity, appearance, shape, size, chemical properties, color, and properties over time are dependent on a properly designed wall, a properly selected plastic material, and a correct process. Any one or a combination of incorrect decisions will render the plastic part unfit for use.

The wall of a plastic part must perform these functions:

- Supports the design structure

- Allows plastic to flow properly

- Provides surfaces for part ejection

- Provides a gate or point through which plastic can enter

- Provides all the required assembly features, snap fits, hinges, threads, etc.

- Meets the appearance requirements of the customer

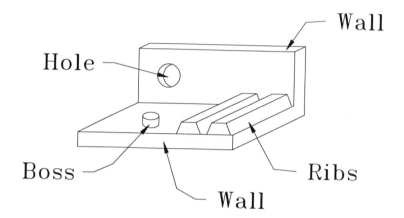

Fig. 6-1 Plastic wall components

Supporting the Design Structure

The wall of a plastic part *is* the plastic part; however, the wall is also the substrate or platform for other part features (see Fig. 6-1), including:

- Ribs
- Bosses
- Gussets
- Threads
- Holes
- Depressions
- Snap fits
- Inserts

These plastic part features are discussed in detail later in this book. The wall of a plastic part should be a nominal thickness; such a wall is referred to as the nominal wall.

Figure 6-2 illustrates how a designer may interpret a wood or metal part (A) for a redesign to plastic, using the nominal wall. The variations (B-F) reflect the designer's assessment of which wall features and surfaces are critical.

The nominal wall of a plastic part is designed to maintain a specific dimension, as defined by the plastic material, and to vary only within specified design limitations. See Table 6-1.

Table 6-1 Nominal Wall Thickness

Thermoplastic	Nominal Wall
ABS............................	0.040 to 0.135
Acetal	0.025 to 0.125
Acrylic........................	0.030 to 0.150
Nylon..........................	0.015 to 0.115
Polycarbonate	0.040 to 0.160
Polyester.....................	0.025 to 0.125
Polyolefins..................	0.025 to 0.140
Polyphenylene sulfide .	0.030 to 0.150
Polystyrene	0.030 to 0.160
PVC (Rigid)................	0.040 to 0.150

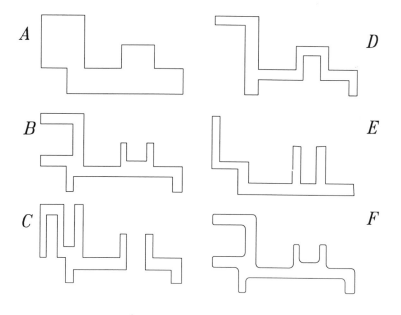

Fig. 6-2 Nominal wall variations

The rate of change in the thickness of a nominal wall should be gradual to ensure proper mold filling and strength. Figure 6-3 illustrates a reasonable guideline for varying wall thickness of a plastic part.

Many designers have attempted to use a uniform wall to consistently produce a plastic part from one product to the next. The uniform wall has exactly the same thickness throughout the part. Unfortunately, a uniform wall may be ideal, but it is unrealistic in the application of plastic product design. Plastic parts are designed to fit applications that require assembly and attachment to other parts. The uniformity of the plastic wall thickness must be compromised to meet most applications.

The nominal wall is a more realistic approach to plastic product design. The nominal wall thickness, by definition, is "in name only." For example, a nominal wall thickness would be specified by the plastic product design with full understanding that there will be thickness variations and transitions throughout the product design. The nominal wall becomes a goal or a target value for wall thickness that is applicable when no other wall thickness is specified. See Fig. 6-4.

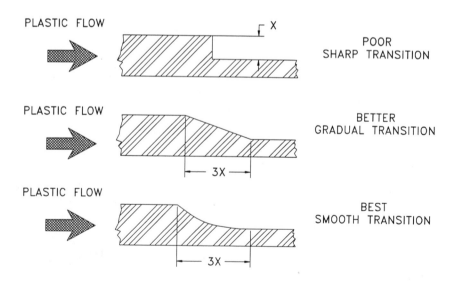

Fig. 6-3 Plastic wall transitions

Proper Plastic Flow

Injection-, compression-, and transfer-molded parts utilize the wall of the product as an area for plastic to flow and fill the part cavity. This added requirement of allowing proper plastic flow requires the plastic part designer to be familiar with the plastic materials and the nature of the plastic molding process.

If the wall is too thin, the plastic flow will be restricted and the part will not fill out properly, or may not fill out at all. This condition is called underfill or short shot.

The restricted flow caused by a thin-walled plastic part may cause the processor to increase the molding pressure, which could result in a highly stressed part or a flash condition. The flash is excess or unwanted material on the part.

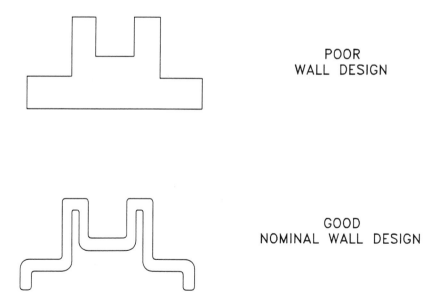

POOR
WALL DESIGN

GOOD
NOMINAL WALL DESIGN

Fig. 6-4 Nominal wall

The restricted flow caused by thin-walled plastic parts will create higher levels of shear forces in the material. The shear forces are caused when layers of plastic are forced to slip over other layers of plastic. The result of high shear levels in a plastic part is higher stress and the potential for lower mechanical and thermal properties.

Thick Walls

If the wall is too thick, the part will require additional plastic to fill the cavity and a longer time for the plastic part to cool. The reason for this is that plastic is a thermal insulator and does not readily absorb or give off heat.

Thick-walled plastic parts also risk having sink marks (depressed areas in the part wall) or voids (empty spots within the part wall).

Thick-walled parts create a more random flow pattern for the plastic, which will lower the dimensional stability and predictability of the part. The part will have more warpage and distortion as well as a higher shrinkage rate.

Figure 6-5 illustrates several thick-wall conditions.

Sink marks are unwanted depressions that occur when a mass of hot plastic in a thick wall section is not thoroughly cooled during the molding cycle. The outside is cool, but the inside is still hot, resulting in the wall collapsing or sinking inward.

Voids, caused by similar conditions as sink marks, occur when the cooled outer surface of the part is strong enough to resist sinking and the inner, hot plastic cools and shrinks. This will create an empty hole, or void, within the plastic wall. A void is structurally one of the most dangerous part defects because it is not visible, thus leaving the erroneous impression that a solid wall has been formed.

Controlled Cells. Some plastic processors have used a foaming agent to create a cell structure or modified structural foam in a thick wall. This process involves adding a foaming or blowing agent to the plastic pellets. Upon melting, the agent decomposes, giving off a nitrogen or carbon dioxide gas that will create small voids or cells within the thick wall. These cells will prevent the formation of sink marks or unwanted voids.

Ribbed Nominal Wall. The thick wall may be redesigned to conform to a more nominal wall with ribs. This redesign is often costly in terms of mold modifications, but it eliminates the potential for sink marks and voids.

Gas-assisted injection molding is a variation of the injection molding process in which nitrogen gas is intentionally injected into the thicker areas of a thick-walled part. The void created by the gas injection is a planned event that can be accounted for in the design. The gas does not mix with the melt in this process, so the void does not become a cellular structure.

The Gate

Plastic material, in the transfer and injection processes, enters the cavity through a gate. The gate is usually a restricted orifice designed to allow the part to fill properly. Once the part is properly filled, the gate is designed to freeze off or close. The closed gate will not allow any additional plastic to enter or leave the part cavity. See Fig. 6-6.

Where to place the gate on the wall of the plastic part is an important decision. Historically, the gate has been located on the thickest portion of the part wall. This allows the plastic melt to flow from the thickest wall section to the thinnest wall section. If the part is gated in the opposite manner, the plastic pressure will drop as the material flows from the thin section to the thick section. This drop in plastic pressure will result in a random flow of plastic

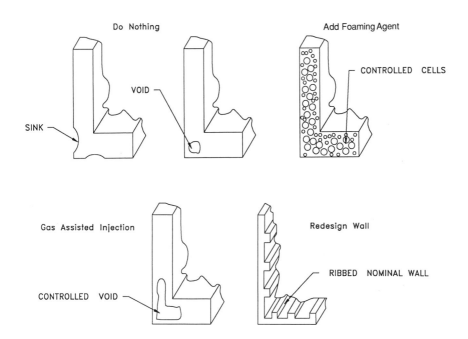

Fig. 6-5 Thick walls

melt within the wall of the part, which can lower the strength of the product and cause cosmetic defects.

Several different gate types are illustrated in Fig. 6-7:

- Tab gate
- Fan gate
- Pin-point gate
- Submarine gate

As the plastic melt enters the gate, the restricted volume creates additional shear stress on the plastic. This additional shear may negatively affect shear-sensitive plastics such as polyvinyl chloride (PVC) or glass-reinforced engineering plastic.

The shear associated with plastic being forced through the gate or a thin wall at high pressure (10,000 to 30,000 psi) may cause degradation of mechanical properties, discoloration, or in the case of glass-reinforced plastic, separation of the glass reinforcement from the plastic matrix.

The Vent

Plastic product designers must also consider how venting will occur in the part and in the mold.

As plastic enters the cavity of a mold, the air that is in the mold is compressed and super heated. If this hot air is not allowed to exit easily, the plastic will not be able to fill the cavity completely (an underfill) or the hot, compressed gas will burn the plastic. In other situations the air could be engulfed in the plastic melt resulting in weak spots in the wall of the part.

The size of the vent to be used is a function of the melt viscosity of the plastic. The vent must be large enough to allow the hot air to escape and small enough to prevent the plastic melt from flashing. A typical vent in a mold is 0.0005 in. deep.

Predicting the location of the vent is difficult. A simple plastic part design has the vent directly opposite the gate; in this situation, the plastic melt enters the cavity and forces the air to compress in front of it. In complex plastic part designs, the venting is more difficult to predict. Computer modeling of the plastic entering the cavity is a high-tech method of determining the proper vent location, but the model is only as valid as the assumptions within the program.

The most practical and popular method of determining the locations for vents in an injection mold is to first sample the mold (prior to installing vents) and analyze the part for underfills and burn marks. This will tell the designer

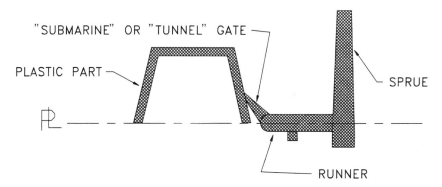

Fig. 6-6 Gate

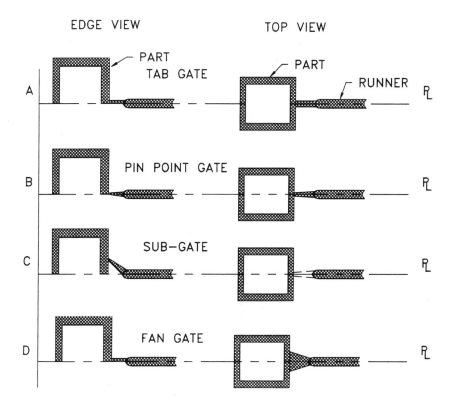

Fig. 6-7 Gate types

more accurately how many vents there should be and where they should be located.

To ensure that this pragmatic technique is used, the designer should add the note "Vent After Sampling" to the part and/or mold print.

Weld or Knit Lines

The wall of a plastic part not only provides support and strength to the part, but also the necessary area for the plastic melt to flow.

The plastic product designer also must understand that the shape of the wall and all its projections and depressions affect the direction and rate of flow.

Plastic melt entering the wall or cavity of a mold may be split into several melt streams or deflected by the turns and twists in the wall geometry. At some point in the filling of the plastic part, these melt streams will join. Each stream will be at a slightly different temperature, which will cause the two melt streams to join differently than if they were at the same temperature. The result

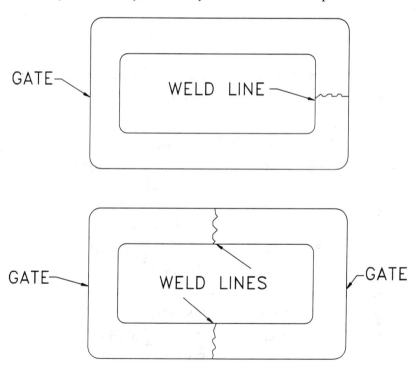

Fig. 6-8 Weld or knit lines

will be a weld or knit line that is often visible on the exterior of the part. See Fig. 6-8.

The weld line is a weak point in the plastic wall. It may be the point where the plastic product fails. The weld line may also be the point where hot gases are combined, and the result could be a burn, a hole, or simply a very weak wall. Predicting the locations of weld lines, like determining the locations of vents, is a complicated affair. The intricacies of the flow pattern can be determined only through computer modeling or by empirical testing.

The product designer may have to alter the flow of the melt by changing the wall of the part by altering thickness, adding projections, or changing gate locations.

Draft

The plastic part must be able to be ejected from the mold, regardless of the molding process. One of the design tools used to accomplish proper plastic part ejection is called draft. Draft is a slight angle or taper on the wall of the part that ensures easy part ejection. See Fig. 6-9. A common draft angle is 1/2 to 1°; however, other angles may be required depending on the nature of the part design.

Three draft conditions are used in plastic part design. See Fig. 6-10.

Positive draft is the common form of draft used to facilitate part ejection.

No draft is a straight wall that is usually dictated by the application of the plastic part or a necessity to have the plastic part remain on the core or male portion of the mold.

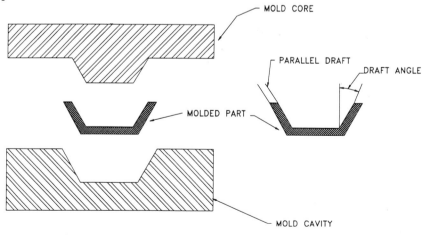

Fig. 6-9 Draft

   Negative draft will have a slightly reversed angle. This may be dictated by the application, but more than likely it is done to ensure that the plastic part remains on the side of the mold that has the negative draft.

Radii

   Plastic melt is viscous. The long-chain polymer molecules, along with any added fillers and reinforcements, tend to flow together and at the same rate. If

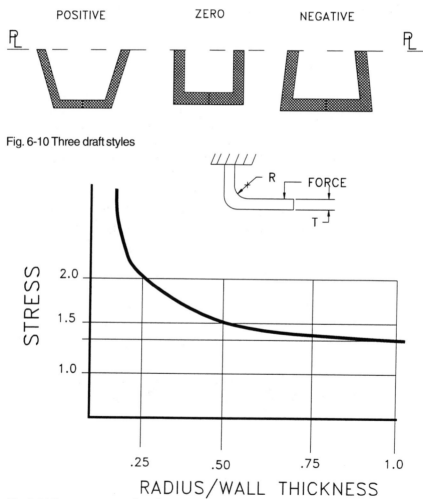

Fig. 6-10 Three draft styles

Fig. 6-11 Stress versus radius size

the wall of a plastic part is too narrow or if the wall has sharp corners, the rate of flow at the wall and corners will be reduced. This will result in a different rate of flow for the molecules near the wall or corner versus the rate of flow of the molecules toward the center of the wall.

This difference in velocity will cause the long-chain polymer molecules to somewhat reluctantly slip over each other, causing a pulling and tearing of the polymer molecules. This is called shear stress.

A good analogy for shear stress is vehicles on the interstate highway system. On a multilane highway, vehicles travel at similar speeds for long distances. All the turns on the highway are gradual (like a radius) and vehicular traffic moves smoothly. If the gradual turns were changed to sharp 90-degree turns, vehicles would change speeds; and this would probably result in accidents, with vehicles falling all over each other. This is similar to the shear stress behavior of polymer molecules.

If sharp corners cause shear stress, then it only makes sense to design plastic parts without sharp corners! Whenever possible, a plastic part should have a radius on its edges. This may not be possible 100% of the time due to

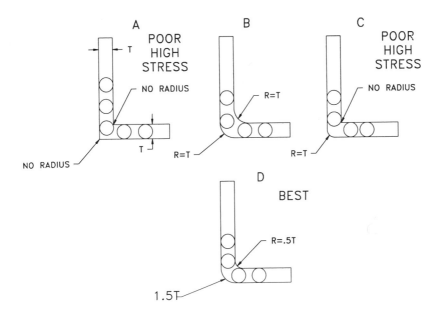

Fig. 6-12 Corner radii

the function or tooling cost of the part, but it should remain a design goal. Figure 6-11 illustrates the relationship between stress and radius size.

The radius is defined by the relationship to the nominal wall (see Fig. 6-12) with the understanding that the objective in wall/radius design is to maintain an even flow of plastic and allow the molecules to move at a uniform speed.

A **fillet** is a radius in an inside corner (see Fig. 6-13), and its purpose is two-fold: (1) to provide even flow of plastic through the wall, and (2) to strengthen the part design at the intersection of two walls.

Surface Finish

One of the most overlooked areas in plastic part design is the nature of the surface of the final product. Most surface finishes are a matter of aesthetics;

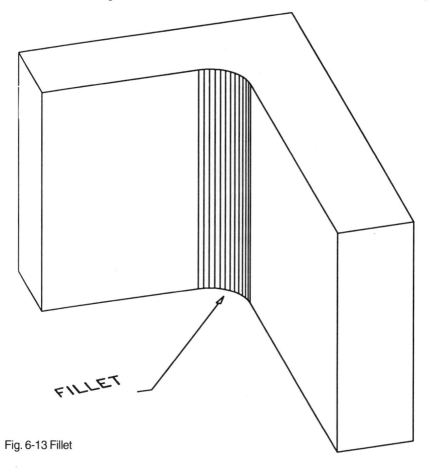

Fig. 6-13 Fillet

with little or no thought given to the effect of the finish on the strength or other properties of the part.

In the past, plastic parts were always designed with a very smooth, highly polished surface. As plastic parts became principal components on the exteriors of consumer goods, the smooth surface was considered an undesirable feature because it would broadcast cosmetic defects and smudges caused by handling. This led to the use of textured finishes.

Texturing the outside wall of a plastic part is accomplished either during the molding process (the mold surface is textured) or during a finishing operation in which the plastic part surface is modified.

When texturing is accomplished during the molding cycle, care must be taken to ensure that the draft of the part is adequate to allow proper part ejection. Also, the texture must have a positive draft itself.

As with any plastic wall design, the texture should be comprised of smooth transitional steps versus sharp corners that could impart additional shear stress to the part.

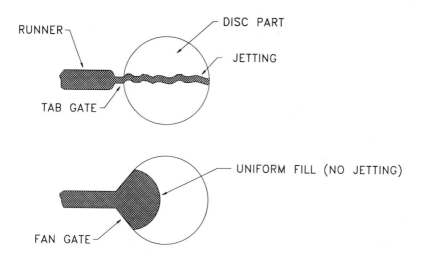

Fig. 6-14 Jetting

Summary of Wall Defects

- **Flash:** unwanted plastic that occurs at the parting line or interface of mold components
- **Underfill:** a plastic part that is not complete in terms of the amount of plastic required
- **Weld or knit line:** the intersection of two or more plastic flow regions
- **Warpage:** plastic part distortion
- **Jetting:** also called "snaking"; a flow mark that is caused by the improper injection of plastic melt into a mold cavity (see Fig. 6-14)
- **Stress:** shear stress that occurs when the plastic molecules skid over each other. Stress may be caused by improper fill conditions and/or sharp corners in a part design
- **Burn mark:** a charred or burnt area in a molded part that indicates improper venting

Extruded Walls

Extruded plastic parts have been described as two-dimensional in design. The extrudate exits the die and is usually cut to a specified length. Pipe,

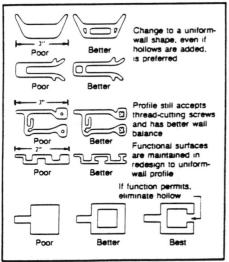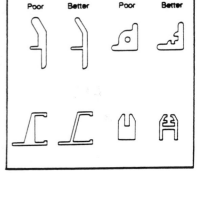

Fig. 6-15 Techniques for improving wall balance. Source: Crane Plastics, Columbus, OH

channel, and hose are all examples of extruded plastic profiles. The dimensions for these profiles must also respect the design criteria for wall geometry.

Wall Thickness

Extruded profile designs have requirements similar to those for molded walls. The goal is to maintain a nominal wall that is balanced. An unbalanced wall will cause material flow variation between the thick and thin sections; if not corrected, these variations will require special die features to compensate for the lack of balance. This results in a more expensive process. Plastic will cool more quickly in thin sections than in thick sections. An extruded profile with both thin and thick wall areas requires additional cooling features within the extruding process to prevent bowing, warpage, and distortion of the desired wall shape. An unbalanced wall also results in a loss of tolerance control as plastic melt shifts during the extrusion process.

A balanced wall design offers the designer and the processor the greatest opportunity for a successful, quality product. Figure 6-15 illustrates some design corrections to achieve a balanced wall.

One of the features that can be incorporated into a plastic wall design is an integral, or living, hinge. See Fig. 6-16. The living hinge is simply a narrowing of the wall that allows the wall to flex or bend. Living hinges may also be

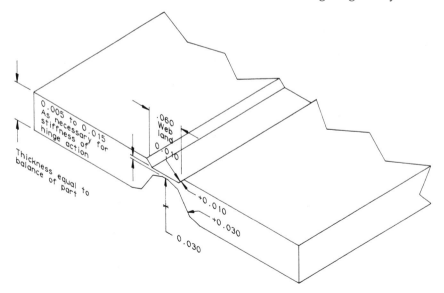

Fig. 6-16 Basic polypropylene hinge design

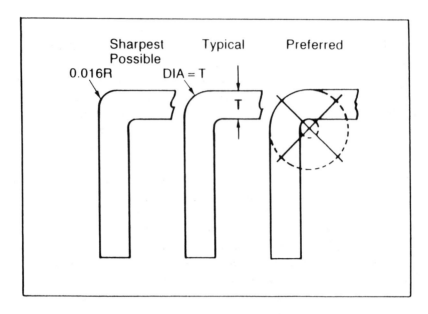

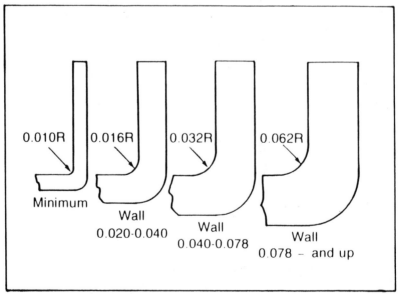

Fig. 6-17 Designing outside and inside radii. Source: Crane Plastics, Columbus, OH

incorporated within the wall design of injection-molded plastic parts; however, the wall thickness and tolerances will be smaller. Polypropylene is the most common plastic used for living hinges.

Radii

Plastic materials tend to bridge sharp corners in a die and to form a radius during extrusion. The sharpest controllable outside corner is 1/64 in. This is a relatively sharp corner and should suffice for most applications. Larger recommended outside corners aid material flow through the die, minimize warpage, and eliminate stress concentration at corners. See Fig. 6-17. The inside radius should also be specified as 1/64 in. minimum, particularly to eliminate a natural notch or breaking point.

Blow-Molded Walls

Blow-molded plastic products offer a unique challenge to product designers and processors. In conventional blow molding, the extruded parison is pinched between the two mold halves, and air is introduced to expand the parison, causing it to conform to the inside walls of the mold. See Fig. 6-18.

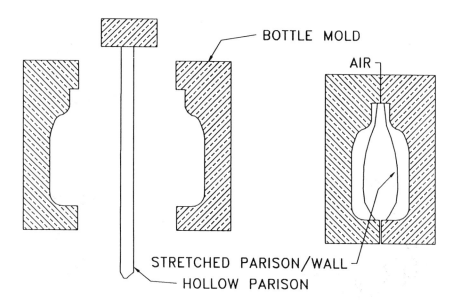

Fig. 6-18 Blow-molded wall

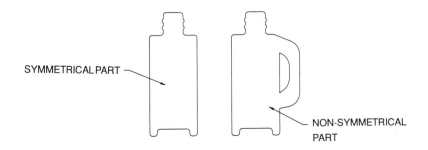

Fig. 6-19 Blow-molded part symmetry

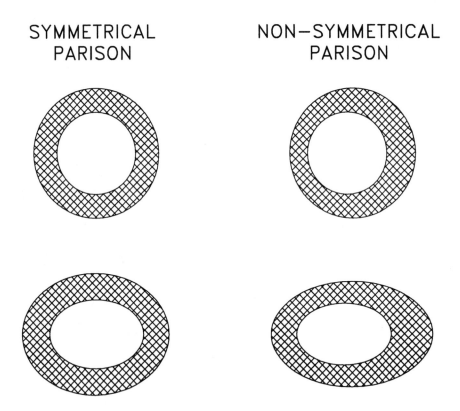

Fig. 6-20 Modifying parison shapes to allow a uniform stretch

The stretching of the parison results in a varied wall thickness if the part is symmetrical. If the product design is not symmetrical, then the wall variation will be exaggerated even more. See Fig. 6-19.

To achieve a uniform wall thickness in a blow-molded part, the parison shape and wall thickness may have to be modified to allow a uniform stretch that will meet the geometry of the desired part (see Fig. 6-20). If the blow molding process is not sophisticated enough to allow for parison adjustments, the product design must consider that the wall of the plastic part will vary across its length.

Thermoformed Walls

Thermoformed plastic parts manufactured on a conventional thermo-former must be designed with a varying wall thickness or have adequate dimensional tolerances to compensate for the wall thickness variations in-herent within the process.

Parts thermoformed on a male mold will have the best dimensional control on the interior of the part. Conversely, parts thermoformed on a female mold will have the best dimensional control on the outside of the part.

The wall thickness in both cases will be a function of the stretch ratio of the plastic. The stretch ratio is the area of the sheet plastic before forming versus

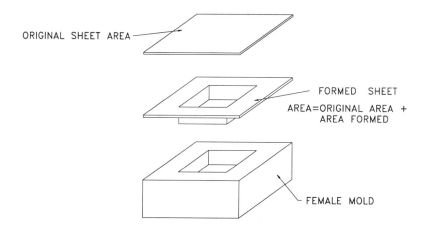

Fig. 6-21 Thermoformed part/wall stretch

the area of the sheet after forming. See Fig. 6-21. This additional after-forming area will come from the sheet thickness.

The uniformity of the thermoformed part can be improved with variations to the thermoforming process; these variations include plug assisting, billowing, or pressure forming. The plastic part designer must consider that parts formed by the thermoforming process will most likely have more wall thickness variations than those formed by other processes. Parts for thermoforming should be designed with adequate tolerances to accommodate this variation.

Composite Walls

Composite plastic products may have the greatest latitude when it comes to wall design. Processes such as spray lay-up, hand lay-up, and pultrusion afford the designer the opportunity to vary the wall thickness without regard to shape. This is because the composite process is not a flowing or melting process that requires the plastic to be conveyed at high temperatures and pressures.

Regardless of the process used, the wall of each plastic part is unique, and the designer must consider all the design elements relative to the material, the process, and the end-use application.

7

Projections and Holes

The nominal wall cannot provide all the features required of the plastic part. The form, fit, and function of the part in specific applications will demand that the nominal wall be modified to incorporate holes, ribs, bosses, threads, gussets, snap fits, or any of hundreds of design features that can be molded or formed directly into the wall of a plastic part. See Fig. 7-1. The majority of the design discussion in this chapter focuses on injection-molded parts; however, specific notes on plastic parts processed by other means are made as required.

Projections on the Nominal Wall

A projection off the nominal wall may take any of several possible forms.

Ribs are added to the nominal wall to create added stiffness or rigidity that would be developed by increasing the overall wall thickness in other materials, such as wood and metal. The design of the rib(s) is a function of the plastic material and the thickness of the nominal wall. See Fig. 7-2. A rib usually has a height of less than 3 times the nominal wall thickness, but it may have a length parallel to the nominal wall that spans the length of the plastic part. The design of the rib also includes some taper or draft. This aids in the removal of the part from the mold. The base of the rib, where it intersects the nominal wall, has a thickness that is no greater than that of the nominal wall. The top of the rib has a thickness that is approximately 0.6 times the nominal wall.

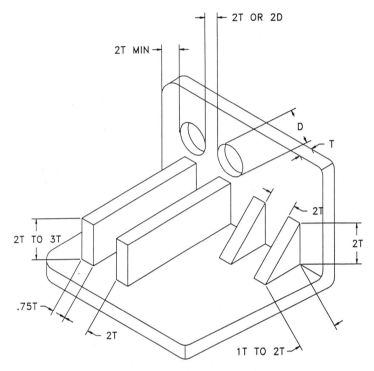

Fig. 7-1 Holes and projections

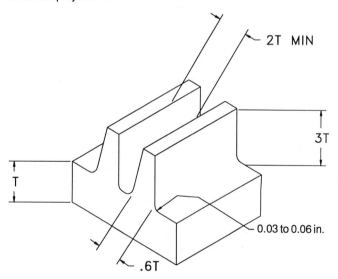

Fig. 7-2 Rib design

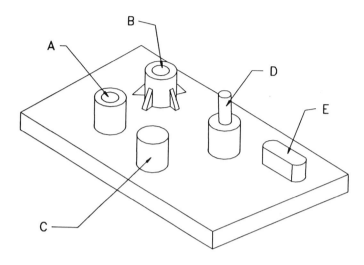

Fig. 7-3 Boss design

If more than one rib is used on any surface, all the ribs should be parallel to each other and spaced at intervals that are at least twice the nominal wall thickness.

Bosses are posts or other geometric shapes of limited length that are parallel to the nominal wall. They are used for mounting and location purposes. Most boss designs are cylindrical because that is the easiest shape to add to a mold; they may be either solid or hollow. See Fig. 7-3. The hollow boss is often used for securing other fastening hardware, such as inserts and screws.

The aspect ratio, *i.e.*, the length of the boss divided by its diameter, can be critical, from both a design and a molding standpoint. The greater the boss length, the more difficult it is to fill and vent. Increasing the length of a boss increases the risk of an underfill condition or a burn.

A conservative guideline stipulates that the boss length should not exceed 3 to 4 times the boss diameter. This may be impractical for many designs, however, so further consultation with the material manufacturer and the mold designer may result in methods to allow longer bosses without risking the product quality.

Gussets are projections added to a plastic part design to support a wall or a boss. See Fig. 7-1. The gusset should be designed to start and stop prior to the edge of the wall or boss it is supporting. This reduces the probability of

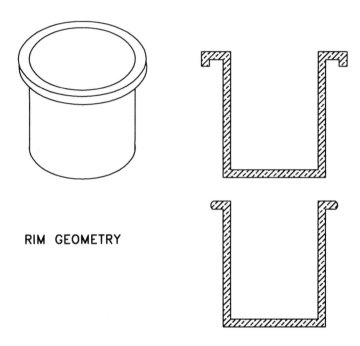

RIM GEOMETRY

Fig. 7-4 Rim designs to improve part rigidity

molding defects. The gusset design can be described as a function of the nominal wall thickness, and the base length of the gusset is usually 1 to 2 times the nominal wall thickness. The height of the gusset is usually twice the nominal wall thickness. The thickness of the gusset should not exceed the thickness of the nominal wall. If several gussets are used to support a single wall or projection, the spacing between gussets should be greater than twice that of the nominal wall.

Rims are projections, or nominal wall continuations, around the outside of a plastic part that provide improved support, stiffness, and dimensional control near open areas in a design. See Fig. 7-4.

If the rim is internal to the part design, it is called an undercut. This design feature is often used on snap fitting caps and safety closures.

The size of the internal rim or undercut depends on how it is to be molded. If the part is to be molded using conventional tooling, the size of the rim is a function of the character of the plastic and its ability to snap over the mold and return to its original shape. See Fig. 7-5. For larger rims, the mold has to include special core retraction features that allow the part to eject. See Chapter 10.

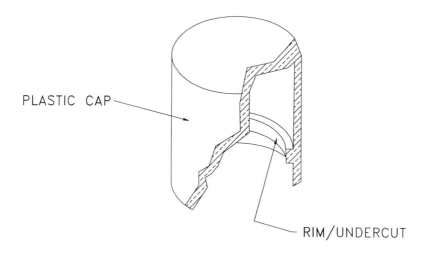

Fig. 7-5 Undercuts for plastic part designs

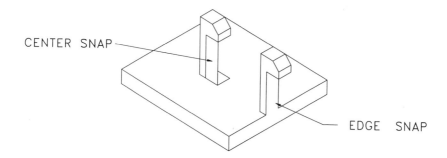

Fig. 7-6 Snap fit projections

Snap Fits. A projection used to snap fit one plastic part onto another will be designed according to the amount of snap (*i.e.,* force and deflection) the nature of the plastic material selected, and the design of the type of snap fit desired. Two snap designs are illustrated in Fig. 7-6. The simplest design is the edge snap fit, which is located on the edge of the part. The tooling needed to mold an edge snap fit projection is simple and requires no special side core action.

The center snap fit is a more complicated projection that requires compli-cated side core action in the mold design. The part designer could allow a through hole to be incorporated in the part design directly below the overhang of the snap. This hole allows the mold maker to directly core the snap fit, thereby eliminating the need for unique and expensive side core action. See Chapter 10 for more information regarding snap fits.

Threads. Molded threads are projections that require special design attention. Conventional threads machined into metal can have sharp tips and sharp angles at the root of the thread. This design is not directly applicable to plastic. Sharp corners on threaded plastic parts will become stress risers, and there is risk that the thread will fail. The suggested alternative design (see Fig. 7-7) involves blunting the tip of the thread design, blunting or flattening the area between threads, at the root and limiting the number of threads per inch to less than 30. These guidelines are applicable to both internal and external threads.

In addition, threaded plastic parts should have a 1/32-in. area exposed prior to the start of any threads. This space will reduce the chance of damage to the first thread during initial engagement.

Gears and Splines. Gear and spline teeth are radial projections on a plastic part. The material manufacturer for a specific plastic is the best source of technical information when designing gears. The most common thermoplas-

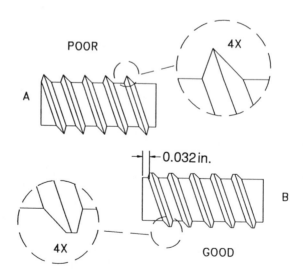

Fig. 7-7 Molded threads without sharp corners

tics selected for these applications include nylon, acetal, and thermoplastic polyester.

There are a few general guidelines for designing gears. See Fig. 7-8. These include:

1. Do not split the parting line across the teeth. A split parting line may flash, rendering a plastic gear useless.
2. Design the gear symmetrically. This will assist in the melt flow and fill of the part.
3. Gate the part in the center. If this is not possible, use multigating 120° around the hub of the gear. This will reduce any distortion caused by nonuniform shrinkage.
4. Make every attempt to radially rib the gear. This will assist the melt flow and reinforce the gear.

Molding Projections

A projection is an addition to the nominal wall. If the nominal wall is adequately designed, the wall thickness will allow the plastic melt to flow smoothly within the wall cavity. When the plastic melt encounters a projection, which is usually perpendicular to the melt flow, the projection is often the last area to fill with plastic. This is because the plastic melt always flows in the path of least resistance, and the perpendicular projection is not the most direct path. See Fig. 7-9. Because the projection is the last area to fill, it may cause one or more molding defects.

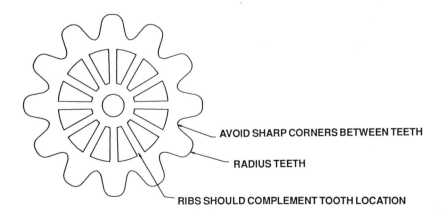

AVOID SHARP CORNERS BETWEEN TEETH

RADIUS TEETH

RIBS SHOULD COMPLEMENT TOOTH LOCATION

Fig. 7-8 Plastic gears without sharp corners

Underfill. The projection may not allow the trapped air and gasses to escape, resulting in an incomplete part. The amount of underfill may not be enough to be visible, but it is often enough to distort details at the tip of a projection.

Burn Marks. The high temperatures caused by the high melt pressure and the difficulty in venting the trapped air in a projection may result in a burning or charring of the plastic that is filling a projection. The resulting burn may be a cosmetic defect and/or a potential mechanical defect in the molded part.

Solutions to defects associated with projections fall into three main categories:

1. Properly controlling the rate of fill during the injection phase of the molding cycle.
2. Properly venting the mold to reduce the possibility of trapped air.
3. Properly designing the projection to facilitate both the fill rate and the venting.

Holes in the Nominal Wall

When holes are added to the nominal wall, the plastic product designer must consider how they are to be produced and whether they are to be molded in or machined in after molding.

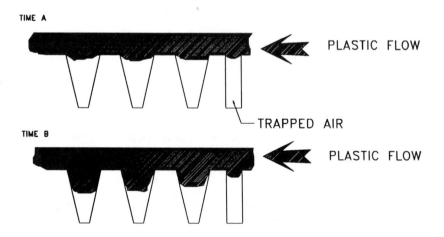

Fig. 7-9 Ribs and projections that are difficult to fill

Molded Holes

Molding any required holes directly into the plastic part may produce a superior hole, as compared with those added during postmolding machining operations. The molded hole may also be less expensive, depending on its size, shape, and location on the part.

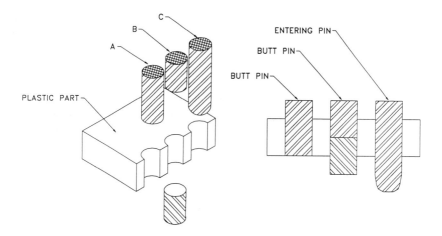

Fig. 7-10 Molded holes requiring special tooling

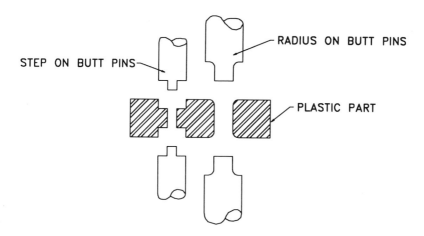

Fig. 7-11 Radius on both sides of a molded hole

The hole type specified by the part designer could significantly affect the cost and quality of the final product. The production of a hole by the mold falls into two distinct categories: those molded using butt pins and those molded using telescoping pins. In Fig. 7-10 and 7-11, design A shows how a mold can be designed to produce a hole in a molded part by having the core pin of the mold pass completely through the nominal wall and butt against the other side of the mold. This design accommodates both a sharp-edged hole or a hole that has a radius on only one edge. A hole manufactured with this type of mold design may tend to have flash parallel to the parting line on the side of the hole where the pin butts against the other mold surface.

The designer must consider the trade-off, in terms of cost and quality, between the added cost of the mold to produce molded holes and the added labor and quality costs associated with postmold machining operations.

Design B illustrates a hole made by two core pins that meet within the hole. This design accommodates hole configurations that have a double counter-bore or a radius at both ends of the hole (see Fig. 7-11). Design C in Fig. 7-10 shows a hole produced with a telescoping, or entering pin. This design is used for long holes because the core pin is supported at both ends and will have little or no deflection. Holes made in this manner are smooth throughout; if there is any flash, it will be perpendicular to the nominal wall.

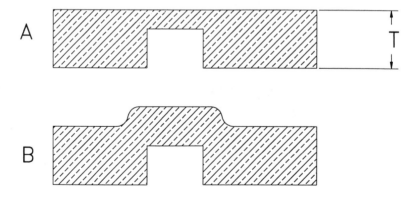

Fig. 7-12 Blind holes requiring wall design changes

Blind Holes

Blind holes are holes that do not go all the way through the nominal wall. A blind hole is incorporated into a plastic part for several reasons:

1. To reduce the amount of material, *i.e.*, coring
2. To hold assembly inserts
3. To locate parts together via pins and holes

In many ways, the blind hole offers the plastic part designer more of a challenge than the through hole. This is mainly due to the fact that the blind hole will require the designer to rethink the design of the nominal wall. See Fig. 7-12. If the blind hole is included in a conventional nominal wall, the stress around the blind hole will be high because the plastic melt will have a restricted flow around the core pin in the mold that creates the hole.

A properly designed blind hole will include a redesigned nominal wall that allows a less restrictive path through which the plastic melt can flow.

Stress

Regardless of the method used to produce a hole in a plastic part, there will always be higher stress around the hole.

Molded Holes. The stress is caused by the nature of the flow of the plastic around the mold components that are used to create the hole in the molded

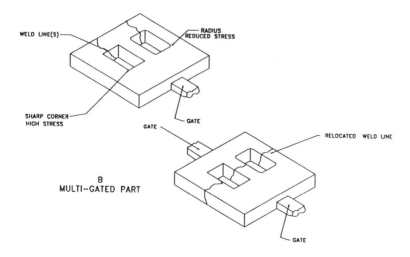

Fig. 7-13 Weld lines and holes

part. Plastic melt that is flowing in a uniform fashion will encounter a core pin in the mold. The plastic melt will split to go around the core pin, and the melt flow will join together on the opposite side of the core. When this happens, the two melt flow fronts have slightly different temperatures; when they join, they will tend to create a weld or knit line. See Fig. 7-13, part A.

The strength of the molded part at the weld/knit line is lower than that of the majority of the part because the long chain molecule entanglement is minimized and could be a site for mechanical failure.

The location and strength of the weld line may be changed by adding or relocating gate(s). See Fig. 7-13, part B. Note that the weld line(s) are still present, but relocation to a less critical area may be preferred.

Shear stress also is increased when plastic melt attempts to flow around a mold core. The level of shear stress is a function of the plastic melt viscosity, the molding conditions, and the shape of the hole being created.

Machined Holes. Machining holes in plastic parts after they are molded or extruded also imparts stress to the part. As the drill bit begins cutting the plastic, a high level of friction is generated that results in both a cutting and a melting of the plastic. The melting is localized, which means that nearby

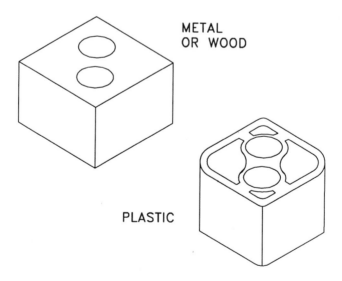

Fig. 7-14 Holes in plastic parts versus holes in metal or wood

plastic molecules are not melted. This differential condition causes an increase in the stress level around the machined hole.

Plastic Conversions

Nonplastic parts with holes that are being converted to plastic designs will often require the product designer to rethink the hole design. As illustrated in Fig. 7-14, the plastic part should be cored out to reduce the mass of plastic around the hole(s) and a new nominal wall should be designed around the hole(s). These steps are required to reduce the risk of hole distortion and out-of-round conditions that may occur due to uneven cooling and shrinkage of the different masses of plastic around the holes.

Holes at the Nominal Wall

Holes adjacent to the nominal wall should not be designed directly within the nominal wall itself. Instead, the designer should add a hollow boss (see Fig. 7-15) that is linked to the nominal wall by a rib. This technique ensures better melt flow and reduced distortion.

Holes Not Perpendicular to the Parting Line

The designer must further consider whether the hole will be perpendicular to the parting line or parallel to the parting line. See Fig. 7-16.

Holes that are not perpendicular to the parting line of the mold will usually increase the cost of the mold and the molded part. This is mainly due to the fact that the simplest action of a mold is to open perpendicular to its parting line, and therefore it is easiest to create holes that are perpendicular to the parting line. Any other type of hole will require the mold to have special

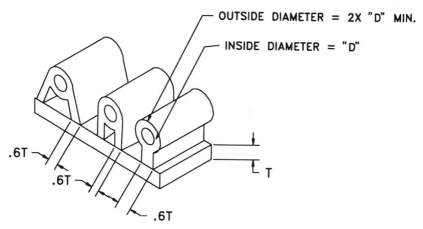

Fig. 7-15 Design guidelines for bosses with holes

features, such as side action in the form of cores that retract parallel to the parting line of the mold to create holes and depressions that are also parallel to the parting line. See Fig. 7-17.

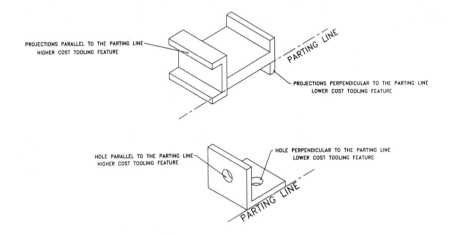

Fig. 7-16 Holes and projections affecting tooling design and cost

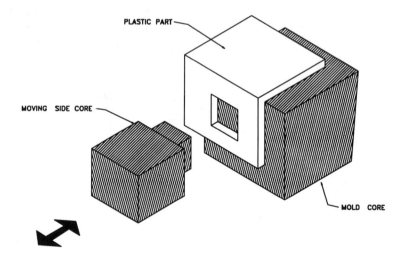

Fig. 7-17 Side holes

One technique used for holes needed parallel to the parting line is to incorporate slots, not holes. See Fig. 7-18. The slot design alternative will allow the part to be molded and ejected in a normal manner without elaborate side cores.

The added cost associated with these more complicated molding systems should be understood by the plastic part designer. There are lower cost alternatives to making holes parallel to the parting line that can be employed if the part designer can make a few design modifications. For example: the design of a plastic laundry basket (see Fig. 7-19) needs to include several holes throughout the basket. The designer may not consider the molding process and cost and thus may submit a design with a strong nominal wall and a fairly straight-sided basket. This design may demand that the mold be constructed with complicated side-cores to make the designed holes. Another designer may specify a thinner nominal wall and a more significant draft angle in the basket's design to allow the mold to use a less costly and vertical coring technique (see Figure 7-20) to produce holes that are parallel to the parting line. In this design, simple vertical mold sections meet to create holes without complicated side cores.

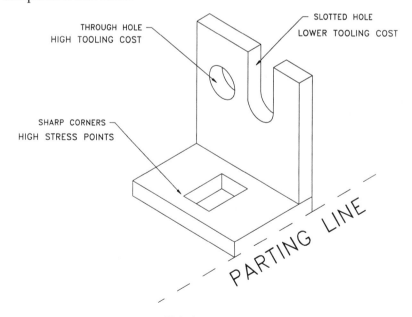

Fig. 7-18 Molding plastic parts with holes

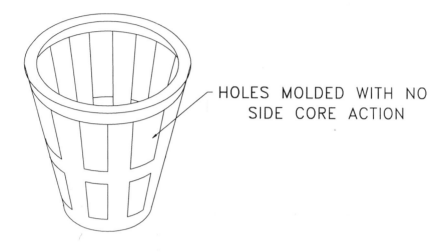

HOLES MOLDED WITH NO
SIDE CORE ACTION

Fig. 7-19 Plastic laundry basket

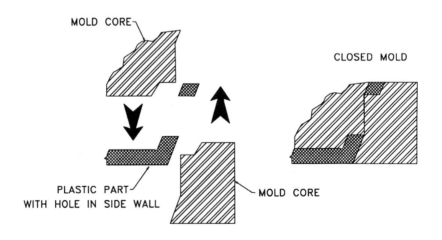

MOLD CORE

CLOSED MOLD

PLASTIC PART
WITH HOLE IN SIDE WALL

MOLD CORE

Fig. 7-20 Molding holes parallel to the parting line

Blow-Molded Parts

Holes molded into blow-molded parts are produced differently from holes manufactured during the injection molding of plastic parts. Holes in blow-molded parts are often produced by an entering or telescoping pin designed within the mold that will stamp or penetrate a compressed or flattened parison (see Fig. 7-21). Since the hollow portion of a blow-molded part is required to hold air under a slight pressure to form the part, it is uncommon to see holes molded into the hollow portion of a blow-molded part. Any holes that are molded into the part are usually in areas where the parison is pressed, such as handles and flat areas.

Thermoformed and Extruded Parts

Any through hole(s) required in thermoformed or extruded parts are usually added with secondary operations, due to the nature of each of the processes.

Conclusion

Projections and holes are design features that make plastic parts useful and aid assembly. The designer needs to appreciate the process capability of each molding system to understand what is being asked of the process. The cost of

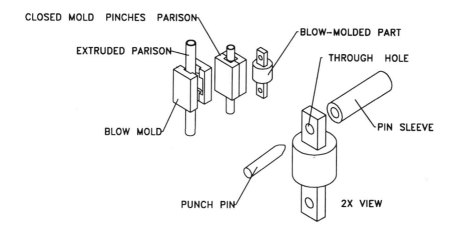

Fig. 7-21 Molding holes in blow-molded parts

added projections and holes runs from very inexpensive to cost-prohibitive, depending on their shape and location.

It may be more practical and cost effective for the designer to use more parts with less-complicated features than to design a single plastic part that is too complicated to be practical.

The designer must also understand that adding holes and projections significantly affects the plastic flow within the mold, and these added features may add significant internal stress to the plastic part that can cause premature failure.

8

Plastic Part Design, Technology, and Quality

The quality of a plastic part or product begins with its design; if the product design is inadequate, then product quality will be inadequate.

Today's global market demands that the quality of a plastic product include consideration in these areas:

- Rapid development (concept to production)
- Complete engineering (no postconsumer changes)
- Manufacturability
- Durability
- Cost

Rapid Product Development

The time it takes to manufacture and market a product is critical. The competitive aspects of the global market provide the greatest opportunity to the manufacturers who get their product to the market first.

Historically, product development included a long incubation period during which time a new product was modeled, prototyped, and tested repeatedly until the design was deemed adequate for production or hard tooling.

The production tooling design and construction was often a trial-and-error affair. A plastic injection mold, for example, might be designed and built based on the experience of the mold maker. This may be the best process for products of a similar nature, but when the design of the desired plastic part is a significant departure from the mold maker's experience base, there is a risk.

A typical flow diagram of part design to product build is illustrated in Fig. 8-1. The quality of the design decisions, in this scenario, is only determined after the mold is built and the plastic product is measured and sampled. There is often a need to go through several design-build iterations to achieve the desired product objectives. This approach is costly in terms of money, time, and product quality.

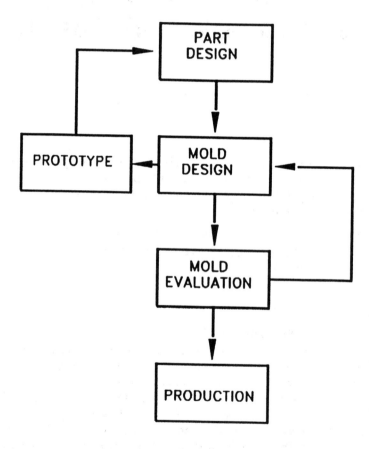

Fig. 8-1 Classic design-to-production process

The design-to-production cycle is complex for plastic parts. As mentioned in earlier chapters, the designer has to comprehend variables such as:

- Plastic materials
- Plastic processes
- Plastic flow
- Stress and shrinkage
- Creep and fatigue
- Complex geometries

Any one of these topics can be overwhelming to the product designer.

Computers and Plastic Product Design

Over the past 10 years, computer technology and design-oriented software have been developed that allow designers to tap into a wealth of materials, processes, and design technologies that would otherwise take a lifetime to learn and experience.

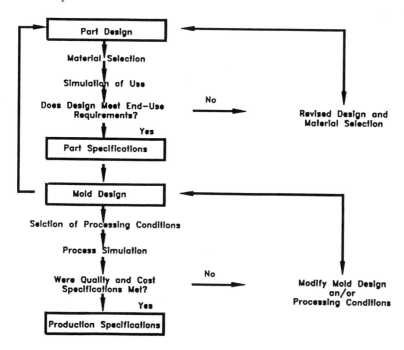

Fig. 8-2 Integrated design decision tree. Source: Plastics & Computers, Montclair, NJ

Today a design-to-production might follow the design scenario outlined in the flow diagram in Fig. 8-2.

The part design is conceived and drawn using a three-dimensional computer-aided design (CAD) software package. Such a design is mathematically correct. This means that, unlike a pencil drawing which is only a representation, the CAD drawing has lines and points that are in a correct relationship to each other, usually to within 0.0001 in. or better. This CAD drawing will become the database from which all other work—such as mold design, mold, build, and part inspection—will be done.

The CAD part design can then be used by the mold designer. Using the same drawing combined with software packages that catalog mold components (plates, bases, inserts), the mold designer can manipulate the part design to create the mold design. Some of the tools available enable the mold designer to invert details, copy sections, and scale details to meet shrinkage requirements.

After the CAD mold design is complete, it too is mathematically correct in all three dimensions. The mold design can then be converted into a numerical control (NC) database to be used by the computerized numerical controlled (CNC) machining centers. These machining centers will read the computer

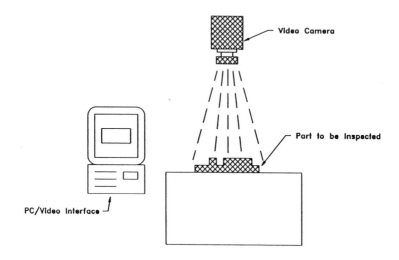

Fig. 8-3 Machine vision inspection

program based on the mold design and perform the required machining operations on the selected mold plates and base. The amount of time and effort a skilled mold maker spends on that mold construction is minimized, and more effort is placed on the coordination and final fitting role.

After the mold is constructed, it is sampled in the mold press. After a stable process has been developed, sample parts are inspected. Today the coordinate measuring machine (CMM) allows inspectors to measure the plastic parts manually or optically, *i.e.*, hands-off. See Fig. 8-3. The CMM's computer will compare the actual part dimensions measured against the original part design. The inspector will receive a printout highlighting any dimensional discrepancies.

The design tools available today range in sophistication from improved (manual) design boards to sophisticated computer-based design systems. The

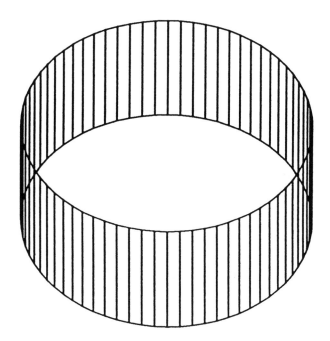

Fig. 8-4 Extruded circle

variety and similarity of systems requires a basic understanding of the design system nomenclature in order to reduce confusion.

Manual Design

Manual design concepts involve the conventional paper and pencil techniques of representing a design idea. There is no true mathematical relationship between that which is drawn manually and the desired design. In other words, the manual drawing does not represent the actual desired dimensions of the design. Manual design work quality can be directly related to drafting mechanics and not the ability of the draftsperson to design. Manual design work is also prone to human error, which may be difficult to check.

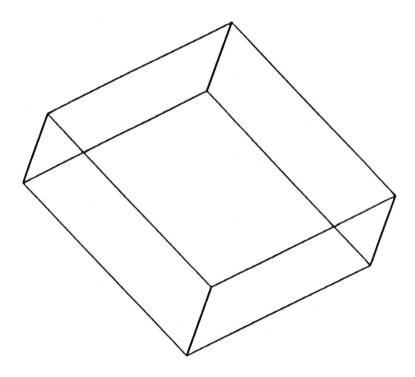

Fig. 8-5 3-D wireframe—a skeleton of the design

During the 1980's the conversion from manual design to computer-based design began. By 1999 it is expected that over 90% of design work will be on computer-based systems.

2-D CAD

Two-dimensional CAD was the first computer-based design system to be widely accepted in industry. As the name implies, the 2-D systems only work in two dimensions—the same as manual design systems. The 2-D systems are often referred to as computer-aided drafting tools because they are oriented to be a direct replacement for manual systems. 2-D CAD is an excellent transition to more sophisticated systems. 2-D CAD also provides designs that have true mathematical relationships and that minimize the drafting mechanic skills required. All CAD users can draw straight lines!

2 1/2-D CAD

The additional one-half D refers to the capability of a 2 1/2-D CAD system to extrude into a third dimension. As an example, a designer could make a drawing of a cylinder by extruding a 2-D circle into the third dimension. See Fig. 8-4. Both 2-D and 2 1/2-D software packages require only a basic personal computer with few enhancements.

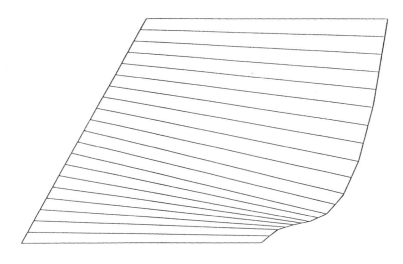

Fig. 8-6 Ruled surface providing surface properties to a part design

3-D Wireframe

This is a true three-dimensional design tool that gives the designer the capability to design 3-D objects by using lines and arcs. The mathematical relationship between all points is correct, and the design can be viewed on the computer from almost any position. See Fig. 8-5. 3-D software packages require larger memory caches if they are to be operated on a personal computer.

Surface Models

Surfacing is the next step in 3-D CAD designing. The surfacing of a wire frame design creates surfaces between lines and arcs to simulate a real object.

The surface may be a ruled surface (see Fig. 8-6), which is created by adding lines across a proposed surface.

The surface may also be a surface of revolution, which is formed by rotating a 2-D plane about an axis. See Fig. 8-7.

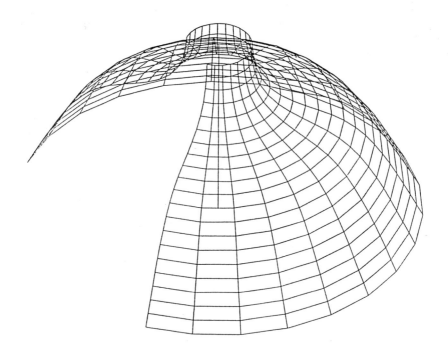

Fig. 8-7 Surface of revolution, or rotated surface

Solid Modeling

Solid modeling was the next logical step in the evolution of CAD. At first the solid model was only considered useful to represent an image of the object being designed. In fact, solid modeling gave birth to the technology now used in computer animation.

Solid modeling is now used to assist designers in designing and understanding how products will look and be assembled prior to production. It is even used for prototyping.

A solid model can be assigned physical characteristic—for example, material attributes such as density and color—to better simulate actual designs. One of the features of solid modeling is that the designer can use

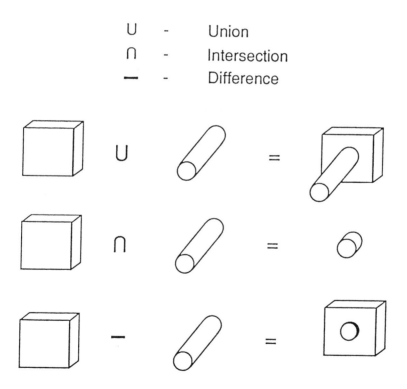

Fig. 8-8 Solid modeling, using Boolean functions

Boolean functions to join and remove object volumes. See Fig. 8-8. This creates the unique impression of being able to cut and machine solid designs with the computer.

Prototyping

The competitiveness of today's global market demands that new products be developed and brought to market quickly. Historically, the time required to bring new products to the market was increased by the preproduction modeling and prototyping needed to allow product developers to:

- See the product
- Evaluate form, fit, and function
- Show the product to potential customers

Prototype construction, and the possibility of several reconstruction iterations, can be a significant task that requires skilled designers, modelers, and machinists to work several weeks or months.

Many plastic parts today are prototyped by building low-cost quick-and-dirty tooling that may be expedited through a tool shop. Such prototyping may be facilitated with the use of CAD designs and CNC tool cutting, but the process is still time-consuming. The life expectancy of such tooling may be less than 500 parts.

Rapid Prototypes

Over the past 5 years, several rapid prototyping systems have been developed that integrate CAD and polymer technology in such a way that a product designer who designs parts on a 3-D CAD system may be able to press a button and generate a prototype part within a few hours. These are direct systems in that no machining operations are required.

Two manufacturers are leading the way in rapid prototyping technology: 3-D Systems, Inc. with stereolithography and DTM Corporation with selective laser sintering.

Stereolithography

The stereolithography apparatus (SLA) is illustrated in Fig. 8-9. The steps in the process are as follows:

- The part design must use a true 3-D CAD system.
- The design must then be surfaced or created into a solid within the CAD system.

- The design file is loaded into the SLA computer, where it is then sliced. This means the object to be built is segmented into several layers.
- The sliced data is fed to the SLA laser/mirrors/elevator system.
- The liquid photopolymer in the SLA tank is cured by the laser as each slice, or layer, is created by the articulation of the mirrors.
- After each layer is created, the elevator system within the SLA tank is lowered (<0.036 in.), and the next slice or layer is created.
- After all layers have been created, the SLA model is placed into an ultraviolet postcuring apparatus (PCA) to cure any liquid polymer that may be trapped within the layers or cells of the part.

The photopolymers are often urethane or epoxy materials and are not as robust as the actual molded parts, which use production plastic material.

The SLA part is adequate to perform several functions including:

- Product visualization for both engineers and marketing
- Testing form, fit, and function

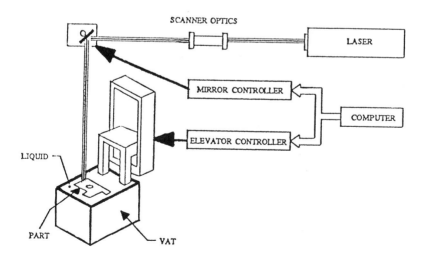

Fig. 8-9 Stereolithography apparatus (SLA). Basic 3-D prototype production using a viscous photopolymer (a wet system). Source: 3-D Systems Inc., Valencia, CA

- Used as a master for casting more robust materials, including metal
- Used as the core in lost core casting

Additionally, because the SLA part is CAD based, larger parts can be scaled down and smaller parts can be scaled up to facilitate evaluations.

Selective Laser Sintering (SLS)

The SLS process was developed by DTM (Desk Top Manufacturing) Corporation and is illustrated in Fig. 8-10. Some of the advantages this method has over conventional prototyping methods include:

- Parts are produced at a rate of about 1 in./hour
- Parts are produced from powder (plastic resin)
- Complex parts are easily attainable
- Most production plastics can be used, including engineering thermoplastics and investment casting waxes

The SLS process incorporates the use of a computer-integrated laser and articulating mirror. The process steps are as follows:

- The product design must be a surfaced or solid CAD design.
- The processing chamber consists of two cylinders and a powder leveling system. See Fig. 8-10.

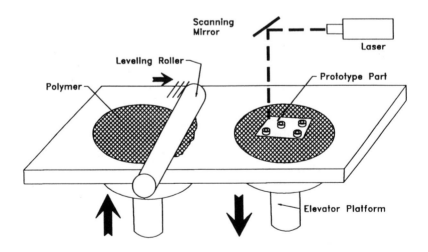

Fig. 8-10 Selective laser sintering. Source: DTM Corporation, Brecksville, OH

- The powder cylinder delivers the powder by moving the vertical stage upward.
- The part cylinder receives the powder in thin layers by lowering its vertical stage, a distance equal to the cross section being built.
- The roller spreads and levels the heat-fusible powder.
- Each layer is sintered with a laser beam, causing the powder to soften and quickly resolidify in the shape of the desired cross section.
- Sufficient energy is supplied to bond each cross section to the previous layer.
- Areas of powder where the laser is turned off remain unaffected and serve to support the object as each subsequent layer is applied and sintered.

Figure 8-11 shows a magnified view of a SLS part.

The technological advances made in rapid prototyping over the past 5 years have been significant. Over the next 10 years the advances should include improved processing speed and the ability to use more robust polymers, metals, and ceramics, thus offering the designer a wide range of ma-

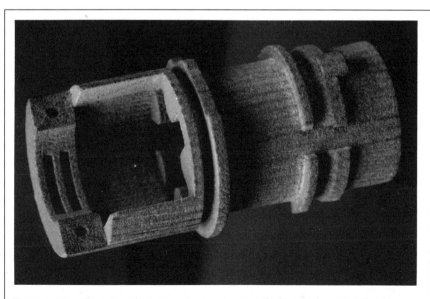

Fig. 8-11 Magnified view of a selective laser sintered (SLS) part. Source: DTM Corporation, Brecksville, OH

terials from which to select. Some industry analysts speculate that the rapid prototyping of today may evolve into the rapid production of the future. Eventually, production parts may be fabricated directly from the design software without any tooling!

TAFA

One area under development to complement the rapid prototype parts is TAFA. TAFA is the trade name for a metal spraying process that has been available to the plastics industry for years, primarily as a metal spraying process for tool making. However, it is now finding a niche market in the area of prototyping.

The TAFA process is capable of spraying an atomized metal coating quickly and uniformly over almost any geometry. The spray is developed in the TAFA gun (see Fig. 8-12) and is extremely fine and atomized, thus allowing the metal coating to pick up the detail of the surface being coated. The gun utilizes a compressed air and electric arc metal feed, as opposed to a flame spray. Because it does not use a flame spray, the TAFA process is kept cool, below 150 °F, and can be applied in thicknesses over 1/16 in.

Computer Analysis of Plastic Processing

As discussed earlier, the computer systems and software available to the plastic product designer are creating opportunities for analyzing product designs and prototypes before any production tooling or processes are developed. The next step in the quality control aspect of plastic manufacturing is to establish a production-worthy design and a production process that meets all engineering requirements such as product life, design-to-cost objectives, and process worthiness.

Historically, the mold design, mold build, and mold process development have been mutually exclusive events. This exclusivity results in an iterative product and process development that is time consuming and costly.

The CAD-generated plastic part design may now be analyzed using a processing software package such as the TMconcept System.

The specific applications for plastic process analysis are based on finite element analysis (FEM). Simply stated, a plastic part is designed on a true 3-D CAD system. The complete part design, not just the surface, is meshed. In essence the meshing of the design segments the part into small elements. These elements can be assigned the properties of specific plastic materials, such as their heat capacity, viscosity, density, etc. The geometry of the part design will

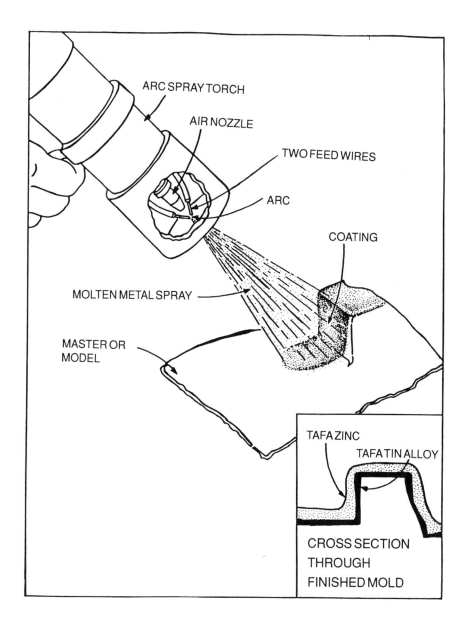

Fig. 8-12 TAFA arc spray moldmaking technique. Source: TAFA, Concord, NH

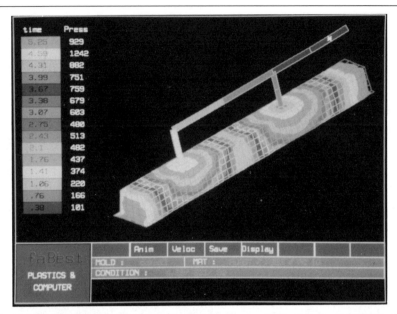

Fig. 8-13 Mold fill pattern. A light fixture cover. Isochrones/isobars show mold-filling pattern and injection pressures. Source: TM Concepts and Plastics & Computers, Montclair, NJ

characterize the pattern of the mesh elements. Once the mesh network has been established and the plastic material defined, the part designer can emulate the plastic process variables including:

- Mold fill pattern. See Fig. 8-13
- Mold cool pattern. See Fig. 8-14
- Part stress level. See Fig. 8-15
- Part distortion

The advanced software allows the part designer and mold designer to model several part/mold design combinations without building a mold.

The plastic processor can also analyze several processing parameters that normally have to be estimated or defined after a mold is built and a process is empirically developed. These key parameters include:

- Part weight
- Gate location

- Vent location
- Molding parameters
- Cycle time

A computer analysis of a plastic part, a plastic process, or a mold is only as good as the data used by the software. The analysis may be ideal for basic plastic molding materials that have few, if any, additives and/or reinforcements. The plastic material database is one of the most important elements needed to obtain a valuable part analysis. Therefore, when computer analysis of plastic parts is performed, it is critical that the material specification used in that database coincides with the actual product requirements.

Processing Quality Control

Prior chapters discuss the importance of controlling incoming material, design elements, and individual processes, but additional tools are required to help analyze the plastic process to locate and identify quality improvement opportunities.

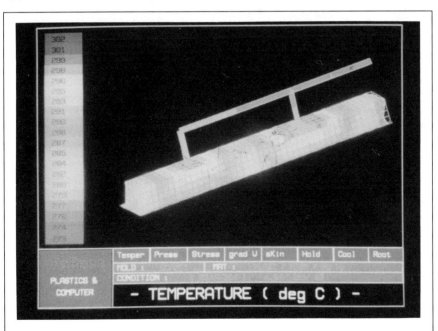

Fig. 8-14 Mold cool pattern. Temperature distribution on the cover. Source: TM Concepts and Plastics & Computers, Montclair, NJ

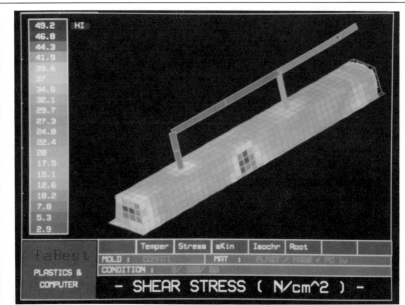

Fig. 8-15 Part stress level. Shear-stress distribution. Source: TM Concepts and Plastics & Computers, Montclair, NJ

One of the first tools to use in the determination of any quality problem is Pareto analysis. See Fig. 8-16. The premise of the Pareto principle is that 20% of the problems generate 80% of the impact, usually measured in dollars. This is true whether processing is done on injection molders, extruders, or hot stamp machines.

To build a Pareto analysis, one must first make a diligent effort to identify and categorize all aspects of the problems to be solved.

Case Study. A small injection molding operation has a 10% yield loss over its entire product portfolio. The first step is to identify the yield loss on each product and bar chart that represents each product yield in declining order of significance. If there are no major differences among the plotted yields, it may be prudent to categorize the rejected parts by their defect category. See Fig. 8-17.

The next step is to determine the cause and effect relationship. One of the tools to aid in visualizing all the different causes and effects is the fishbone diagram. See Fig. 8-18. The main problem to be analyzed is the "head of the fish." To better comprehend cause-and-effect issues, many times it is best to

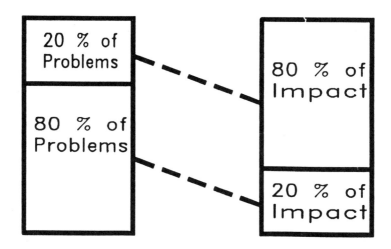

Flg. 8-16 Pareto principle

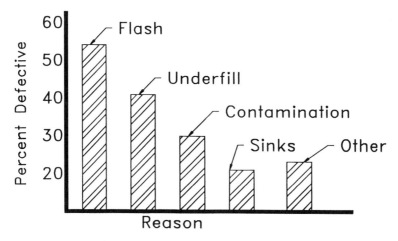

Fig. 8-17 Pareto analysis

conduct a brainstorming session with a team comprised of representatives from these areas:

- Processing
- Quality assurance

- Tooling
- Engineering
- Supervision

Together, this team will suggest possible factors that may affect the yield under the categories of material, machine, method, and manpower. The team must focus on possible causes only. Time spent trying to solve or defend each possible source of the quality problems, at this time, will bring the brainstorming session to a grinding halt.

The general categories indicated above are applicable to almost any manufacturing process.

Material concerns that often arise are:

- Incoming quality from the supplier
- Material handling (using the right material)
- Poor regrind control
- Material contamination

Machine concerns that often arise are:

- Worn or poorly maintained equipment
- Poor or improper process control systems
- Wrong size equipment
- Fluctuations in environment (water temperature, oil temperature)

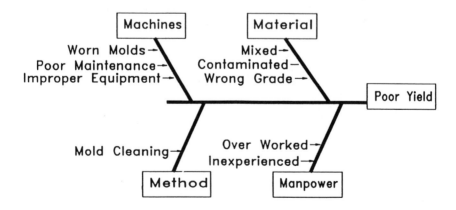

Fig. 8-18 Cause and effect analysis—fishbone diagram

Method concerns that often arise are:

- Little, no, or improper training
- Wrong process parameters
- Improper quality inspection

Manpower issues that often arise are:

- Little, no, or improper training
- Unsafe practices
- Lack of communication between shifts

This list could be significantly longer, and the list of possible solutions begins with the basic inverse of the problem; *i.e.*, if the problem is the lack of training, then the solution is to properly train the operators.

While the many solutions appear obvious, implementing them and maintaining procedures is difficult. The challenge for any plastic part manufacturer is to maintain a high level of technical and communication skills across the entire workforce. This task is a never-ending process!

Statistical Tools

Regardless of whether you are a designer, a supplier, a manufacturer, or a customer, you will find that statistical tools help locate problems. The operative words are "help locate." Statistical tools do not *solve* problems.

A good analogy is the fuel gauge in your car. The gas gauge is a statistical tool; when it reads full, you have the confidence to travel many miles. When it approaches empty, you start to worry and search for a gas station. The statistical tool (the fuel gauge) informs you that you are low on fuel, and you make the decision to either get gas or sleep in your car on the side of the road. The statistical tool (the fuel gauge) does not solve the problem. It only highlights or signals the potential problem.

Statistical tools common throughout the plastic part manufacturing industry are the $\overline{X}$ and R chart used to measure variables, and the P chart used to measure attributes.

Variables are those characteristics that can be directly measured, such as length, weight, and time. Plastic variables include dimensions and part weight.

Attributes are those characteristics that cannot be directly quantified. Plastic attributes might include flash, underfill, burn marks, contamination, splay,

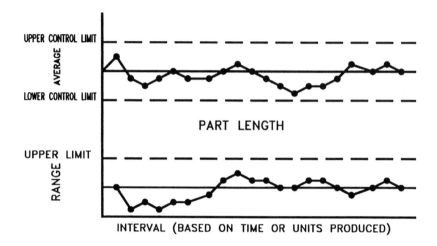

Fig. 8-19 $\overline{X}$ and R chart used for variable data

or streaking of the surface. Yield is also considered an attribute because yield is a calculated characteristic and is not directly measured.

$\overline{X}$ **and R Charts.** These are statistical tools that document and track specified variables over a period of time. See Fig. 8-19. The $\overline{X}$ represents the average or mean of samples inspected during each time period, and the R represents the range (high value minus the low value) for the specified variable of the samples measured during each time interval.

These variables are measured at specified time intervals, *i.e.*, every hour, and are plotted on the $\overline{X}$ and R chart. The resulting chart can be studied in much the same way a physician studies an electrocardiogram to determine if there are any unusual trends or out-of-specification issues that need to be addressed. Statistical reference books and guides can help explain the details of such tools.

P **charts** are statistical tools designed to track and document attributes over a period of time. Each time or production interval, 10 parts are inspected for one or more specified attributes, such as burns and underfill. The yield or percentage defective is quickly determined and plotted on a *P* chart. See Fig. 8-20. This tool is handy and very simple to use; however, it is not as powerful

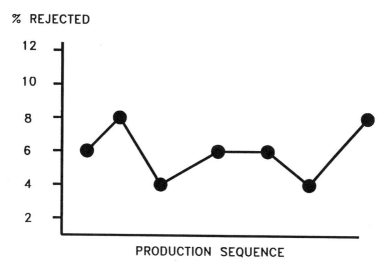

% REJECTED

PRODUCTION SEQUENCE

Fig. 8-20 P chart used for charting attributable data

as the $\overline{X}$ and R chart for highlighting quality problems. Plastic part manufacturers are being driven by their customers to provide quality parts and on-time delivery. To be competitive, the plastic manufacturer must maintain excellent quality records, have the highest quality standards, and adopt a management style that encourages continuous quality improvement.

9

Finishing and Decorating Plastic Parts

Plastics are unique in many ways. They are excellent electrical and thermal insulators. Some plastics are as clear as glass while others are dark and opaque. Many plastics are readily attacked by chemical solvents and sunlight while other plastics are robust in almost all environments.

These characteristics provide the plastic product designer with many challenges in the areas of finishing and decorating. All plastics are not equal, and the plastic product manufacturer needs to understand the plastic surface, the decorating materials, and the decorating process that will be required to finish the product.

This chapter provides an overview of the following topics:

- The plastic surface
- Cleaning the plastic surface
- Static electricity
- Vacuum metallizing
- Electroless plating
- Electrolytic plating
- Hot stamping
- Pad printing
- Printing and coding
- Painting plastic
- Machining of plastic

It is important to note that each plastic material has a different set of requirements and that reference to the plastic material manufacturer's technical literature is critical to the success of any finishing and decorating operation.

The Plastic Surface

There are thousands of plastics, and each material has different surface properties that directly affect the finishing and assembly of a plastic product.

Unlike metals, plastics do not have an abundance of free electrons ready to support the conduction of electricity or reaction with other materials. Metals readily react with oxygen to form oxides (rust); plastics do not rust. This characteristic is an advantage when it comes to galvanic corrosion, but it is a disadvantage in the areas of printing, coding, plating, and painting. Plastic surface hardness ranges from soft, easy-to-scratch materials to extremely hard materials that are resistant to marring and scratching.

The plastic surface is not always stable. The surface may shrink or expand depending on the environmental conditions. Some plastic materials contain additives such as plasticizers and antistatic agents that will bloom or migrate to the surface of a part over time. The result could be degradation of the surface appearance and the ability of the plastic to allow paint or plating to adhere to it.

Cleaning the Plastic Surface

In the past, cleaning a plastic part was only associated with removing flash (see Fig. 9-1) or surface contamination such as oil or processing chemicals.

The processes used to remove flash are:

- Hand deflashing
- Tumbling
- Media deflashing
- Cryogenic deflashing

Hand deflashing requires an operator to manually remove the flash from the plastic part. There are often special cutting, punching, or trimming tools associated with hand deflashing, and there is always the risk of the operator being injured and/or the part being ruined.

Hand deflashing is a costly process; however, it may be the only practical way of producing a quality flash-free part for short production runs.

Some plastic materials such as rigid thermosets (phenolic, epoxy, melamine) always tend to have flash due to the nature of the molds and molding

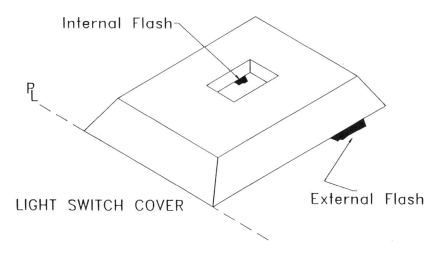

Fig. 9-1 Flash on a light switch cover

process. These high production volumes require that a high-volume deflashing process be used.

One of the simplest high-volume processes used to deflash rigid plastics with external flash is tumbling. The tumbling equipment is simple and often custom made by the molder. The tumbler is usually a variation of a metal drum or cylinder that is perforated in such a way that the plastic parts will not fall through the perforations. The tumbler is then located on a rotating mechanism. See Fig. 9-2. The plastic parts to be tumbled are loaded in the tumbler so that at least 50% of the tumbler is still empty. The tumbler is set in motion, ~4 to 10 rpm, allowing the parts to roll and impact against each other. This constant impacting will remove the brittle, external flash in 5 to 15 minutes. The limitations of tumbling are many: parts must be molded with rigid/brittle plastic material; only external flash will be removed; the part geometry and strength must provide a robust part; and, regardless of the material, overtumbling will destroy the part.

Media deflashing (see Fig. 9-3) has existed for hundreds of years and is used in the metal, ceramic, and plastic industry. Media deflashing is a variation of tumbling that allows both external and internal flash to be removed.

The parts to be deflashed are loaded into a media deflasher, which is a piece of equipment that tumbles the parts in a sealed environment. Once the tumbling starts, a media material is broadcast over the parts, under air pressure,

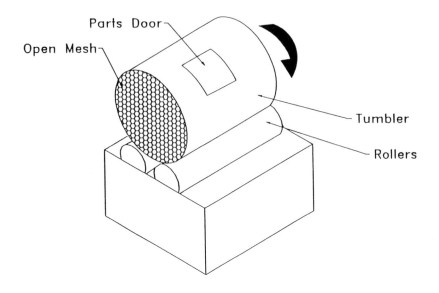

Fig. 9-2 Simple tumbler deflasher

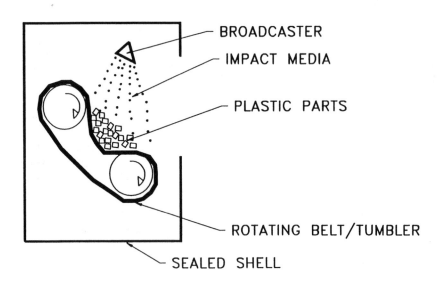

Fig. 9-3 Media deflasher

and at high velocity. The combination of the tumbling and the impacting of the media removes the flash.

The media can be either natural or synthetic, and the size of the media particles should be controlled to meet the specific deflashing application. Typical natural media materials are ground walnut shells or apricot seeds; typical synthetic media include nylon and polycarbonate.

Cryogenic deflashing is used for soft or flexible material, such as elastomers or rubber. A cryogenic deflasher is essentially a tumbler that is used at cold temperatures (–40 to –100 °F). At these temperatures, even rubbery materials become rigid, thus allowing flimsy, flexible flash to be removed that would otherwise be impossible to remove. To achieve the cold temperatures, liquid nitrogen or expanding carbon dioxide is introduced into the sealed tumbling chamber.

The process of cleaning oils and surface contaminants from the surface of plastic parts is complicated by the fact that many plastics are, themselves, attacked by the chemicals and solvents used to remove the oils.

To better understand the problem and the subsequent solution, one should first examine why the surface of a plastic part needs to be clean. Today, plastic parts are used in the production of food, dairy products, medicines, cooking and eating utensils, medical items, and electronic parts. All of these applications demand clean plastic parts. Plastic manufacturers have taken extra precautions for items such as disposable medical products by molding the parts in clean room areas; however, this is economically impractical for most plastic parts.

How do oils and surface contaminants present themselves on plastic parts? The source for contamination is omnipresent in the manufacturing plant. Plastic processing aids, such as mold cleaners, oils, and mold releases, are too often considered required material, for the processing of plastic materials. Some surface contaminants evolve directly from the plastic itself. Additives, such as flame retardants, antioxidants, plasticizers, and antistatic agents, migrate out of the plastic parts over a period of time. This phenomenon results in visible surface contamination.

For plastic parts assembled with metal parts, the cutting oils and rust inhibitors used in the manufacture of the metal parts often linger on the surface of the plastic part.

The solution to the presence of surface contamination on plastic parts may not always be to start off with clean parts. Secondary operations such as washing and degreasing may be required.

Washing of plastic components is not always a simple process. Many plastics are hygroscopic (that is, they absorb water), and a washing process might degrade properties of the plastic. Some plastics that absorb water include:

- Nylons
- ABS
- Polycarbonate
- Thermoplastic polyesters

The soap itself may affect the properties of the part, and, in some cases, soap is a worse surface contaminant than the contaminant that it was being used to wash off!

Chemical degreasing with degreasing fluids that are not harmful to the plastic, humans, or the environment can be effective; however, such a combination of requirements may lead to a process that is too costly or impractical.

The use of a detergent-free ultrasonic washer may be the best method. In this type of washer, clean water is placed in a tank that is subjected to ultrasonic (high-frequency) vibrations. Thousands of small bubbles are created that scrub the part's surface and thus clean it without the use of heavy soaps or solvents.

Static Electricity

Plastics are dielectrics (electrical insulators), and this resistance to conducting electricity has made plastics a material of choice for electrical and electronic applications.

Unlike metals, plastic materials do not have an abundance of free electrons to conduct electricity. If free electrons come to rest on a plastic part, they will remain on the surface without any ability to move—hence the term static electricity. As illustrated in Fig. 9-4, there could actually be "pools" of electrons on a plastic part. This charged surface will have a propensity to attract dust particles and aggravate cleanliness problems mentioned earlier.

The problem of plastic and static electricity ranges from a nuisance level—clothes made with synthetic fabrics clinging to each other when they come out of a clothes dryer—to an irritating level—static discharge when walking across a nylon carpet. Static in the manufacturing environment can be both costly and dangerous. Static discharge near an integrated circuit can destroy the circuit's memory, and the rapid movement of plastic film in an extrusion line could cause static discharge that could result in bodily damage.

In order to render a plastic part less susceptible to holding a static charge, the plastic has to be made less dielectric, *i.e.*, more conductive, especially on the surface. Three main techniques increase the surface conductivity of plastic (see Fig. 9-5):

- Internal antistatic agents
- External antistatic agents
- Surface discharging

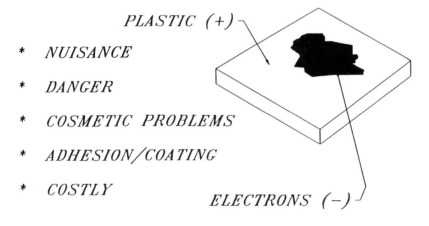

PLASTIC (+)

* *NUISANCE*

* *DANGER*

* *COSMETIC PROBLEMS*

* *ADHESION/COATING*

* *COSTLY*

ELECTRONS (−)

Fig. 9-4 Static electricity

* *DO NOTHING !*

* *GROUND OPERATORS*

* *ANTISTATIC AGENTS* *SURFACE*
 INTERNAL

* *IONIZED AIR*
    ELECTRIC
    NUCLEAR

Fig. 9-5 Static electricity reduction options

An antistatic agent is to dissipate the static pools of electrons on the surface of the part by increasing the surface conductivity of the part.

Internal antistatic agents are additives that are designed either to remain in the plastic and increase the conductivity of the entire part, *e.g.*, carbon black, or to be incompatible with the plastic and migrate to the surface of the part and increase the surface conductivity of the plastic. Note that internal antistatic agents are considered to be long lasting. They are usually effective over the entire product life.

External antistatic agents are sprayed, wiped, or rubbed onto the plastic part to provide a short-term increase in surface conductivity. A recent consumer application provides a practical example of an external antistatic agents—clothes dryer sheets rub against synthetic fabrics during the drying cycle to create a short-term increase in the surface conductivity of the fabric and dissipate the static charge. Water is also an external antistatic agent.

Surface discharging occurs when plastic parts are exposed to an ionized atmosphere, usually electrically charged air. The ions in the air will bathe the plastic part and dissipate the static charge.

Discharging equipment requires a source of ionized air. The two main sources are electrically generated ions and nuclear-generated ions. The nuclear discharging system is quite simple, consisting of a small quantity of low-level nuclear material. Both discharging systems require air to pass over the ion source. The ionized air will then form an ionized "curtain" (see Fig. 9-6), which neutralizes any static charge on a plastic part. The advantage of this system is that almost any part size and geometry can be neutralized.

Vacuum Metallizing

Many customers demand that their plastic parts have a shiny metallic surface. Historically, electroplating was the only viable process to metallize plastics; however, vacuum metallizing now provides designers with an alternative process.

Vacuum metallizing was developed in the 1950's and used as a decorative and functional coating on plastics. The decorative applications included both plastic and metal parts for use in the automotive markets, and the functional applications were in areas where conductive plastics were required. The main problem with these early vacuum-metallized applications was durability; the vacuum-metallized coating would not withstand the rigorous application environments commonly experienced by metal and electroplated plastic parts. A second problem was the perception of customers and manufacturers.

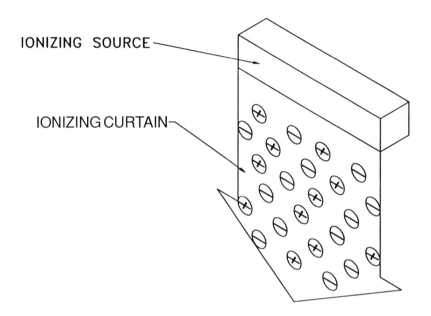

IONIZING SOURCE

IONIZING CURTAIN

Fig. 9-6 Neutralizing electrostatic charges

Vacuum-metallized plastic parts were considered only for low-cost decorative or novelty applications.

Today, vacuum metallization is used in a wide variety of plastic applications, including:

- Automotive interior trim
- Toys
- Flashlight reflectors
- Appliance trim
- Light diffusers

Vacuum metallization is a physical, rather than electrochemical, process that involves depositing a metallic coating onto a prepared surface. Deposition takes place within a high-vacuum chamber. The plastic substrate is normally prepared with a lacquer, which forms a base for good adherence of the metallic layer to the plastic part. See Fig. 9-7. The parts to be metallized are then placed into a vacuum chamber (see Fig. 9-8), where metal is "evaporated" by passing electric current through a metal filament condensed onto the base coat. A nonmetallic, clear topcoat may be added to improve the wear resistance of the metallized layer.

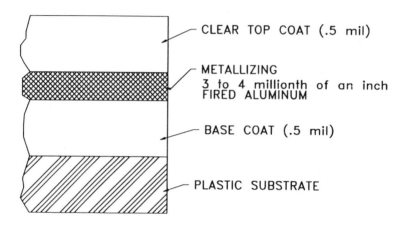

Fig. 9-7 Vacuum-metallized plastic

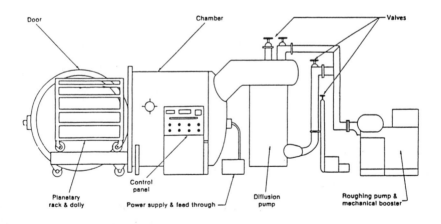

Fig. 9-8 Common 72-in. horizontal metallizing chamber. Source: Vacuum Platers, Inc., Mauston, WI

Vacuum metallization, by definition, is a batch-type process; however, automated material handling equipment can be used to facilitate the process, as in the production of continuous metallized foils.

All the parts to be metallized must be thoroughly cleaned to ensure good adhesion and appearance. The parts must be free of any processing chemicals, such as mold release and oils. Slight surface imperfections may be hidden by the base coat; however, many imperfections can be exaggerated by metallizing.

Since the deposition of the vaporized metal used in the vacuum metallizing process is a line-of-sight process, the plastic parts need to be rotated within the vacuum chamber (see Fig. 9-9) to allow all faces of the plastic part to be

Fig. 9-9 Vacuum metallizing rack system. Source: Vacuum Platers, Inc., Mauston, WI

metallized. The part must, therefore, be fixtured and secured on a rack. The actual point where the plastic part is fixtured may not be exposed to the vaporized metal and will not be metallized. The part designer must consider this when designing the part (see Fig. 9-10).

Typical metals used in the vacuum metallization process include aluminum, chromium, and copper.

Gold may also be used in applications where high conductivity is required. In the late 1960's, the astronauts' plastic face shields were metallized with gold to protect them from both intense radiation and sunlight.

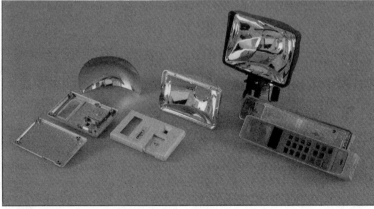

Fig. 9-10 Vacuum-metallized products. Source: Vacuum Platers, Inc., Mauston, WI

The actual amount of metal used on a vacuum metallized plastic part is 3 to 4 angstroms (millionths of an inch), which is significantly less than the 0.001 in. thickness of metal associated with conventional electroplating. The base coat and top coat(s) add an additional 0.001 in. to the overall thickness of a plastic part.

Vacuum-metallized plastic parts can be made to pass rigorous tests, including:

- Tape adhesion
- High humidity
- Salt spray
- Thermal cycling
- Weatherometer (long-term aging)

There are several important cost savings associated with vacuum metallizing versus electroplating that should be considered, including the fact that the thinner coat means less metal is used; and there are few, if any, toxic chemicals involved that might require special handling and disposal. Several vacuum-metallized products are illustrated in Fig. 9-11.

Fig. 9-11 Vacuum-metallized products. Source: Vacuum Platers, Inc., Mauston, WI

Electroless Plating

Electroless plating is a surface treatment process that does not require electric current, as does electrolytic plating, to precipitate the metal onto the plastic part. See Fig. 9-12. Electroless plating deposits a dissolved metal (such as copper or nickel) onto the surface of a plastic part through the use of a chemical solution.

The use and application of electroless plating is widespread throughout the United States. The plating on plastic (POP) industry and the printed circuit board (PCB) industry are two of the largest users of electroless plating.

Most of the POP market is for automotive parts, such as:

- Wheel covers
- Grilles
- Lamp bezels
- Mirror brackets

Other nonautomotive parts include:

- Marine hardware
- Plumbing fixtures
- Packaging
- Appliance and furniture knobs and handles

One of the most important applications for electroless plated plastic parts and all forms of metallized plastics is the radio frequency interference (RFI) and electromagnetic interference (EMI) markets. Soon after the Federal Communications Commission (FCC) passed regulations in 1983 stating that all

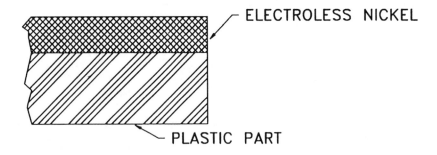

Fig. 9-12 Electroless plating

computing devices have to be shielded so as not to emit large levels of radio waves, metallizing of plastics took on a new perspective. The first electroless plating processes were developed in the mid-19th century to plate thin layers of silver onto glass to manufacture mirrors. Electroless plating of nickel and copper was developed and used during World War II. The use of electroless plating on the nonconductive surface of plastic parts did not occur until the early 1960's. ABS was the first plastic to be electroless plated.

Prior to electroless plating plastic parts, the surfaces have to be treated to ensure good adhesion. Several steps need to be performed, including:

- Pre-etching
- Etching
- Neutralization of the etchant
- Catalyst application
- Activation of the catalyst
- Addition of the electroless copper or nickel

A flow diagram of the electroless plating process is shown in Fig. 9-13. Any plastic part to be plated with the electrolytic process must first be electroless plated to create a conductive surface.

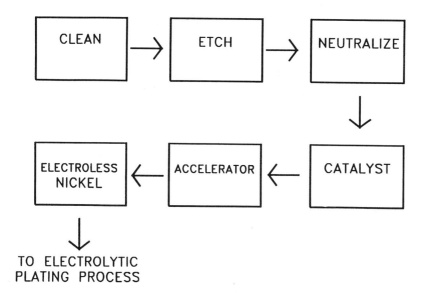

Fig. 9-13 Flow diagram of electroless plating

Pre-etching is a process for preparing the plastic surface for etching. In some instances, the pre-etch operation is a series of wash and rinse cycles designed to remove dirt and oils from the surface of the part. In other instances, the pre-etch could consist of an abrasion process designed to roughen the surface of the plastic part to facilitate adhesion of the plated material.

The etching process often involves the use of a chromic acid solution formulated to remove certain components of the plastic material. As an example, ABS is a readily plated thermoplastic material; the butadiene component of the ABS (the butadiene is the "B" in ABS) is readily attacked by the chromic acid etchant. The rest of the ABS plastic remains virtually untouched when the butadiene is etched out of the surface of the plastic. The resulting surface consists of a series of microscopic pits or undercuts. See Fig. 9-14. These undercuts are the sites where the subsequently applied plating metal(s) will adhere to the plastic surface. The success of the plating directly relates to the ability of the plastic to be etched.

Some thermoplastics that can be readily etched and plated include:

- ABS
- Modified PPO
- Modified polypropylene
- Polysulfone

Neutralization of the etchant is the next step in the electroless plating process, and it is conducted to neutralize the acidic etchant and thus prevent contamination of subsequent steps. Note that between all processing steps in the plating of plastic there is at least one rinse operation to prevent contamination and ensure process purity.

Catalytic application is the next step in the process. The catalytic action has also been referred to as "seeding." The catalyst can be an acidic bath of colloidal palladium. The palladium particles are extremely small (<5 microns) and find their way into the small crevices created during the etching process.

Activation of the catalyst can occur by having the plastic part, with the colloidal palladium catalyst, placed into an accelerator bath to promote the plating process.

Chemical deposition of the nickel, and sometimes copper, is the next step in the electroless plating process. A thickness of metal, ~0.5 mil, is allowed to develop on the surface of the plastic part. This process takes less than 10 minutes.

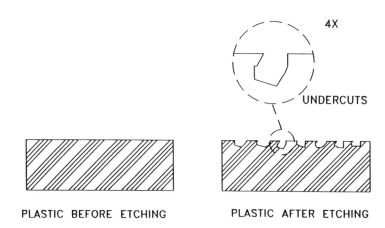

PLASTIC BEFORE ETCHING   PLASTIC AFTER ETCHING

Fig. 9-14 Etching

At this point, the electroless plating process is complete, and for many applications this is the end of the plating process. Typical plastic products that require only electroless plating include:

- Decorative toys and hardware
- Printed circuit boards
- Data recording media
- Electromagnetic shielding
- Lighting systems and reflectors

Electrolytic Plating

Many plastic parts continue beyond the electroless plating process to include the electrolytic plating process. The electrolytic plating process builds upon the now conductive electroless plated plastic part to yield a metallized plastic surface that emulates a plated metal surface. The electrolytically plated surface is thicker and more robust than the electroless plated surface and can therefore be used in more rigorous environments.

The electrolytic plating process starts at the completion of the electroless plating process. See Fig. 9-15. The electroless plating process was all chemical deposition, whereas the electrolytic plating process requires electrical current to deposit metal from a solution.

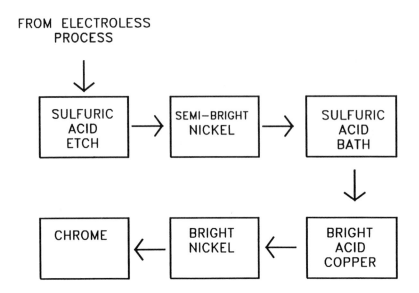

Fig. 9-15 Flow diagram of electrolytic plating

First the electroless plated plastic is etched once again. The etchant is sulfuric acid, and it prepares the surface for the future deposition of metallic layers.

After the acid etch, the part undergoes a semi-bright nickel deposition. This layer helps limit and control the amount of current that is exposed to the plated surface and thus protects it from burning off. A mild sulfuric acid bath follows to prepare the surface for the next layer of metal.

Bright acid copper is electrolytically deposited on the surface of the part to provide the surface conductivity required for the subsequent metallic layer to be deposited.

To electrolytically deposit metal onto a plastic, the plastic part must be made electrically conductive and then grounded, that is, used as a negative electrode. The metal to be plated is positively charged, thus allowing the positively charged metal atoms to precipitate onto the negatively charged plastic.

Bright nickel is then electrolytically deposited. This nickel layer is the immediate surface onto which the chrome will be deposited. See Fig. 9-16.

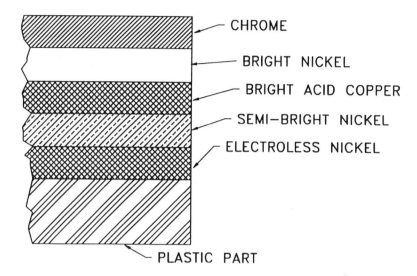

CHROME

BRIGHT NICKEL

BRIGHT ACID COPPER

SEMI−BRIGHT NICKEL

ELECTROLESS NICKEL

PLASTIC PART

Fig. 9-16 Electrolytic plating

The final electrolytically deposited layer is the chrome. The chrome metal is brilliant in appearance and very hard. Today's plating technology yields plastic parts that are indistinguishable from metal parts; however, the plated plastic parts are lighter, less expensive, and can be used in a wider range of designs than their metal counterparts.

Typical applications for electrolytically plated plastic parts include:

- Interior and exterior automobile parts
- Bottle closures for cosmetics
- Furniture hardware
- Toys
- Marine hardware

To provide a standard rating for plated plastic, the American Society of Electroplated Plastic (ASEP) has developed a service condition (SC) code for common applications. The SC ratings are as follows:

SC-1—mild service conditions; usually for indoor applications such as decorative and novelty items

SC-2—moderate surface; usually for indoor applications with some exposure to temperature cycling and moisture. Typical examples include cosmetic bottle closures, kitchenware, and knobs

SC-3—Severe service conditions where the part could be exposed to some chemicals and temperature cycling. Typical applications include toys, cookware, lawn furniture, and hospital items

SC-4—Very severe surface conditions where the part might be scratched, dented, or exposed to corrosive chemicals and temperature cycling. Typical applications include automotive and marine exteriors, and plumbing fixtures

The quality of a plastic part that has been metallized is directly related to the quality of the plastic part prior to metallization. Stated another way, metallization does not mask or cover up cosmetic problems with the original plastic part. Figure 9-17 illustrates a few of the common problems associated with the part or plated part quality. Sinks marks or other depressions on the part surface may be exaggerated on the plated part. Sharp corners may result in molding stresses that could easily be sites for stress cracking as the plastic part journeys through the various plating chemicals. The result may appear in the form of hairline cracks on the surface of the plated part. Common marks that are transferred to the plastic part by the mold itself—such as from ejector pins, parting lines, and gates—will appear as cosmetic problems on the plated surface.

The part design may have to be altered to provide the best appearance after plating. Reshaping the part to avoid the mold marks, mentioned above, is

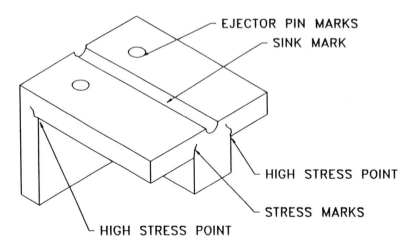

Fig. 9-17 Part defects associated with part/plated part quality

important. The designer should also consider the effect that holes and projections may have on the plating process. Figure 9-18 illustrates some common plating problems that can occur when the transition to holes and projections is too great. To correct this chrome burr problem, the designer of the part should incorporate smooth and gradual transitions and avoid holes and projections whenever possible. The chrome plater must also be involved to ensure that the plating racks are designed to allow for uniform metal deposition on the surface of the part.

Hot Stamping

Hot stamping and several variants (see Fig. 9-19) have been developed in recent years to include postmold decorating and in-mold decorating. The technological improvements in the equipment have allowed for automation and process consistency. Hot stamp foil and heat transfer decals now provide the plastic product designer with a wide variety and range of decorating possibilities; these include decorating in all three dimensions as well as on unusual part shapes. See Fig. 9-20.

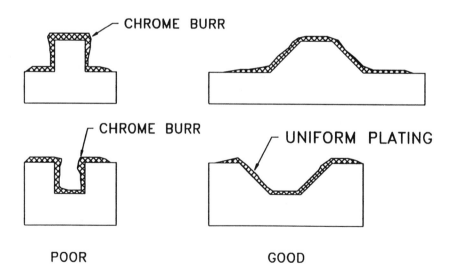

Fig. 9-18 Common plating problems when the transition to holes and projections is too great

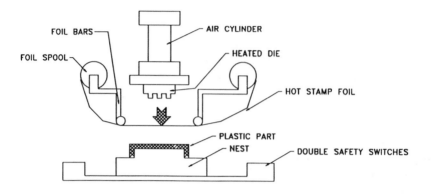

Fig. 9-19 Hot stamp machine

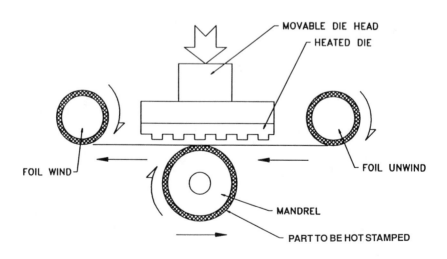

Fig. 9-20 Hot stamping round parts

Hot stamping is no longer limited to a separate postmold process, although this is the most common format. New developments in the area of in-mold decorations provide the manufacturer with additional productivity opportunities.

Hot Stamp Foil

Hot stamp foils are actually multilayered systems. See Fig. 9-21. The top layer is called the carrier because it supports all the subsequent layers. The release layer is designed to have enough adhesion to hold all the layers to the carrier layer, but it is also sufficiently weak to provide a precise release from the carrier when the foil is processed onto the part. The polymer topcoat may be a single-layer or multilayered affair. The function of the topcoat is to provide both protection and a transparent "window" to the metallized coats. The metallized layer has historically been a chrome or gold surface that is either a true metallized surface or a paint. Today's hot stamp foils can be almost any color and texture desired, including patterns such as wood grain. After the metallized coat, the size, or adhesive coat, provides the bond required to hold the foil onto the surface of the plastic part. Again, advances in adhesive technology have allowed the creation of foils that are both attractive and robust. The activation of the adhesive layer on hot stamp foils requires temperatures from 250 to 350 °F. This is lower than the melt temperature of most plastics, and if the actual dwell or heat time is short (1 to 2 seconds), there will be no distortion of the plastic part.

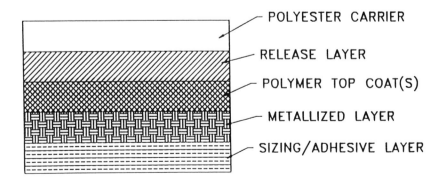

Fig. 9-21 Hot stamp foil composition

Hot Stamp Equipment

Hot stamping equipment is relatively simple in both design and technology; however, the parameters involved in the process must be precise for product consistency. Those parameters include:

- Die location
- Die pressure
- Die temperature
- Dwell times
- Foil control (advance and strip)

The hot stamp process is often a stand-alone batch process in which the plastic parts are manually loaded and unloaded. The process is easily adaptable to various "pick-and-place" devices that can load parts directly into the hot stamp nest after molding, to increase productivity. The hot stamp process, and all the variants of it, can also be continuous in nature. The continuous processes are used in the extrusion industry.

Mold decorating of plastics with hot stamp materials has been developed to the point where parts are molded and ejected from the mold completely decorated.

The rate at which plastic products can be hot stamped will, of course, vary with the specific process and part geometry. However, a stamping rate of 1 part in 1 to 2 seconds is common.

The type of tooling for hot stamping will depend on the production quantity required, *i.e.*, prototype or full production, and the product design.

Early in the product design, a decision must be made as to whether a part will be designed with projections (see Fig. 9-22), which will be hot stamped with a silicone pad, or whether the part will be more or less flat in design and require a die (see Fig. 9-23) to imprint the desired pattern on the part.

The silicone pad technique is the simplest from the hot stamping process perspective and the most complicated from the part design perspective. The silicone pad is silicone rubber bonded to aluminum. The silicone rubber is a high temperature resistant thermosetting material that can be purchased in a wide variety of thicknesses and hardness levels. The rubber/aluminum pad is mounted to the heated platen of the hot stamp machine; the pad will eventually be heated to the desired temperature, which is usually ~50 °F below the platen temperature due to the low thermal conductivity of the rubber.

The plastic part must be designed with projections, the top surface of which will be stamped, that are tall enough (>0.062 in.) to create a separate plane to be stamped without stamping other areas. See Fig. 9-22.

The die method of hot stamping requires that a die be made with the mirror image of what is to be hot stamped on the part. The die must be made in such a way that the die details are themselves projections. See Fig. 9-23. The die can be manufactured using a pantograph, electrical discharge machining (EDM),

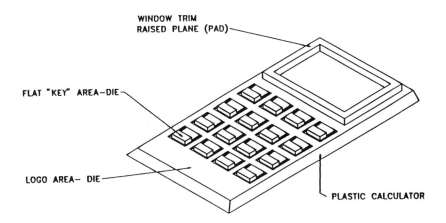

Fig. 9-22 Hot stamping with a silicone pad

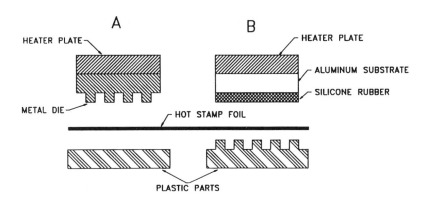

Fig. 9-23 Hot stamp dies

or acid etching. Typical die material is brass for short (1000 pieces) runs; aluminum or steel is used for production runs.

Whether using the pad or die method to hot stamp, consideration must be given to the part "nest," *i.e.*, the tool that will position and secure the part during the hot stamping process. It is possible to use moldable materials such as a casting epoxy for short-run applications; however, production runs will require aluminum or steel.

The nest should also be designed to facilitate loading and unloading of the part whether it is a manual or robotic process.

Hot Stamping/Process Integration

Hot stamping provides an excellent example of how processes that were once considered only batch processes can evolve into integrated processes. Injection-molded, extruded, and die-stamped parts are now being manufactured with the hot stamp process as a component of or immediate extension of the primary process. No nonvalue added labor, such as material handling, is involved. The raw material enters the process cell, and a completely decorated product exits the cell.

Technological advances in the hot stamp process, such as the addition of microprocessors and proportional temperature controllers, have provided both the process controls and the ability to integrate several different processes into a manufacturing cell.

Variations of Hot Stamping

The hot stamp foils and processes have advanced to the level where other decorations can be added to plastic parts with little or no changes to the basic equipment.

Decals, labels, and similar multicolored transfers can be produced onto a carrier and applied in a similar manner as hot stamp foil. This technology has opened the design possibilities to include sophisticated labeling, multicolored images, barcodes for product recognition, and even photographs.

Pad Printing

Pad printing was developed to fill a processing void that could not be filled by the conventional hot stamping process or its variants. Product designers wanted to decorate plastic parts on surfaces with complex geometries; in addition, they wanted precise detail, high production capabilities, and multicolored images in complete registration.

The pad printing process (see Fig. 9-24 and 9-25) begins with the cliche plate. The cliche plate is an etched or pantographed steel plate that has the

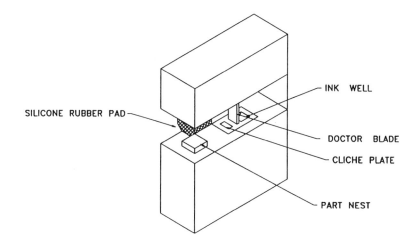

Fig. 9-24 Pad printing

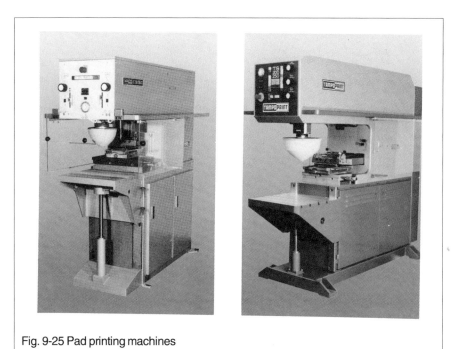

Fig. 9-25 Pad printing machines

artwork to be transferred onto the plastic part. The artwork is etched ~0.003 to 0.005 in. into the plate. See Fig. 9-26.

Behind the cliche plate is the ink well. The ink well is a shallow trough that holds the ink to be used in the pad printing process.

Located between the ink well and the cliche plate is a doctor blade and a wiper blade. This wiper blade moves toward the ink well and scrapes a small quantity of ink, which is then dragged across the cliche plate. The wiping process allows the engraved areas of the cliche plate to be filled with ink, and the motion of the doctor blade removes any excess ink.

In the next step in the pad printing process, the silicone rubber pad is pressed onto the cliche plate. The pressing of the pad allows the ink trapped in the crevices of the cliche artwork to temporarily adhere to the silicone rubber pad.

The rubber pad now advances toward the nested plastic part to be decorated. The pad is then pressed onto the surface of the plastic part. In the process of being pressed against the plastic part, the soft silicone rubber pad conforms to the surface of the part, and the ink is transferred from the pad to the part.

Because of the unique properties of silicone rubber, the pad is completely free of ink after one press onto the part, and the process can begin again.

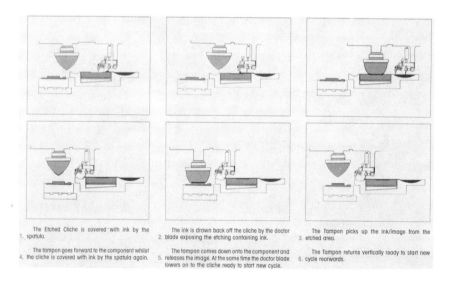

1. The Etched Cliche is covered with ink by the spatula.

2. The ink is drawn back off the cliche by the doctor blade exposing the etching containing ink.

3. The Tampon picks up the ink/image from the etched area.

4. The tampon goes forward to the component whilst the cliche is covered with ink by the spatula again.

5. The tampon comes down onto the component and releases the image. At the same time the doctor blade lowers on to the cliche ready to start new cycle.

6. The Tampon returns vertically ready to start new cycle rearwards.

Fig. 9-26 Schematic method of operation

Pad printers are manufactured with indexing nests to allow for continuous production. The pad printer can also be manufactured with multiple cliche plates and pads to allow the designer the opportunity to decorate plastic parts in multiple colors and complex artwork.

The quality of pad printing is excellent and the detail is superb.

Printing and Coding

The need to print directly on plastic parts goes beyond decorating. Other items printed on plastic include:

- Date codes
- Barcodes
- Recycle codes
- Part numbers

The conventional techniques for printing are modifications of existing printing technology, such as:

- Stamp printing
- Silk screening
- Spray and wipe

The surface condition of the plastic must be considered prior to attempting any printing on plastic. Several plastic materials, such as polyethylene and polypropylene, have surfaces that do not readily accept inks. To create a printable surface on such plastics, the manufacturer must activate the surface of the plastic part. This activation can be accomplished in two low-cost ways: flame treating and corona discharge.

Flame Treating. In this process, the plastic part is exposed to a gas flame. The high heat is applied only for a fraction of a second and creates a highly active surface on which printing is possible. The effect is short-lived, so printing should be accomplished immediately. This process is used in the printing of polyethylene milk bottles. The bottle is literally dropped through a ring of flame.

Corona Discharge. Also used in the plastic milk jug manufacturing process, corona discharge employs an electrostatic generator that discharges onto the plastic part, temporarily activating the surface. Corona discharge can activate the surface of several plastic parts at one time.

In stamp printing the code or lettering is produced on a metal or rubber die. The die is exposed to an ink, usually an epoxy-based ink, and the part is stamped much the way a hand stamp operates.

Silk screening is a process that uses a finely meshed screen that is first covered or filled with a photosensitive chemical. The image of that which is to be reproduced is placed onto the screen and exposed to light. The light cures the chemical not covered by the desired image, thus blocking the small holes in the mesh. The unexposed area is washed to expose the holes in the mesh.

After the screen is made, the part to be printed is placed under the screen, and ink is forced through the mesh onto the part.

Spray and wipe is a process that requires the plastic part to have the desired code or image "cored" into the part so that the image lies below the actual surface of the part. Ink or paint is applied to the part, and the surface is immediately wiped off. The ink or paint in the cored area remains to highlight the code or artwork. See Fig. 9-27.

New technology is integrating computers with the coding and painting systems to allow immediate and frequent code changes. Two of the more popular high tech systems are ink jet printing and laser etching.

Ink jet printing is a direct adaptation of the ink jet printer used to print documents. The ink jet concept actually sprays a crisp and highly directed and focused beam of ink onto the plastic part. The printer has no direct contact with the part. The inks are fast setting and allow the designer to print date codes, part numbers, and messages on most plastics regardless of the shape of the surface.

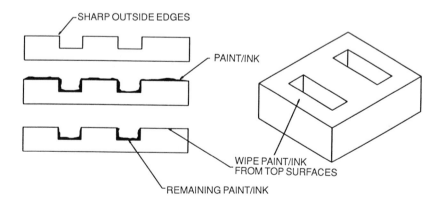

Fig. 9-27 Spray and wipe painting

Laser etching requires that a laser beam be aimed at articulating mirrors that are computer controlled. The laser beam has sufficient intensity to burn the surface of the plastic, thus creating the code or image. See Fig. 9-28.

Painting Plastic

Plastic parts can be molded using a variety of precolored plastics, or the natural plastic material can be custom colored to meet special color requirements.

While molded-in color is convenient for most applications, there are circumstances where it may be desirable to paint the plastic part. Painted plastic parts are widely used in the automotive market, where plastic and metal parts have to be precisely color matched. In this situation, painting both parts at the same time provides the best color match.

Techniques for painting plastic are noncontact or spray techniques. Conventional spray painting using paint, compressed air, and a spray gun works

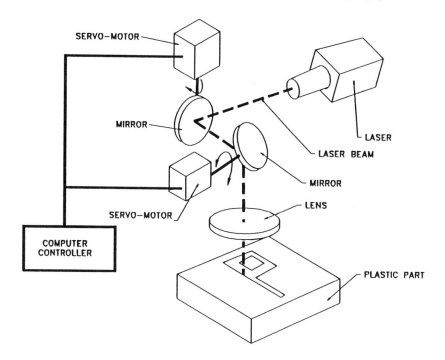

Fig. 9-28 Laser etching/coding

well for plastic. All the conventional paint application techniques can be adapted for plastic parts. Most important to successful painting of plastic is preparing the surface and using the specified paint.

Whether painting onto metal or plastic, the surface of the part to be painted must be clean. As mentioned earlier in this chapter, cleaning the plastic surface requires an understanding of the plastic material to be cleaned and the effect of the solvents on that plastic. Additionally, the plastic may have to be etched to promote adhesion. Molded and extruded plastic parts tend to have glossy, resin-rich surfaces. This type of surface condition is desirable if the part is to be used as-molded; however, the glossy surface may require abrading or etching to hold the paint.

As mentioned in the discussion on printing, some plastics such as polyolefins may require special surface treatments to activate the surface. The flame treatment and the corona discharge method are applicable for prepainting as well as preprinting. The paint to be used must be carefully considered. Plastics may require a primer to help improve the adhesion of the paint to the plastic; and after painting, a topcoat may be required to improve the wear resistance of the paint.

Several categories of paints should be considered when painting on plastic. Water-based acrylic paints offer ease of application, and they contain virtually no harmful solvents and provide brilliant color possibilities. Lacquers, almost all of which are polymers themselves, contain a solvent that evaporates, and there is no chemical reaction within the paint itself. When considering lacquers, the solvent-plastic relationship must be understood. Enamels are based on a chemical reaction that takes place between binder materials to create a film. The effect of this reaction on the plastic material must be considered. Two-part paints, such as epoxy paints, provide excellent adhesion qualities and may not require a topcoat. The reaction and its effect on the plastic material should be considered.

Machining of Plastic

Shaping plastic is mostly accomplished using a molding process; however, sometimes machining of plastic sheet and shapes is required in special applications such as prototyping and repair parts.

Some important facts to remember when considering plastic machining operations are:

- Each plastic is different.
- Plastic expands when heated.

- Highly stressed plastic will distort when heated.
- Metal cutting tools may not work properly when machining plastics.

There are some important guidelines to remember when considering machining of plastics. Tools must be kept extremely sharp. Regular cutting tools with sharp cutting edges are acceptable for short runs, but tungsten carbide or diamond bit tools are recommended for long production runs.

Adequate cutting tool clearance is essential. See Fig. 9-29. Dull tools and/or improper clearance angles cause difficulty because of the resilient and elastic nature of the plastic.

Measurements must be made with care. Compression can result in inconsistent measurement because dimensional measurements can change up to 24 hours after machining has been completed. Localization of heat causes expansion in that area and results in overcuts and undercuts, or in drilling tapered holes.

Heat build-up must be minimized. Heat generated from the machining operation does not dissipate through the plastic workpiece as it does through metal. If the heat is not dissipated, the surface finish of the part can be affected

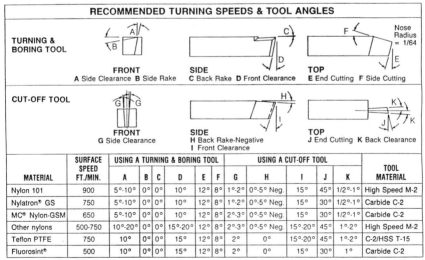

| | | RECOMMENDED TURNING SPEEDS & TOOL ANGLES | | | | | | | | | | |

MATERIAL	SURFACE SPEED FT./MIN.	USING A TURNING & BORING TOOL						USING A CUT-OFF TOOL				TOOL MATERIAL
		A	B	C	D	E	F	G	H	I	J	K	
Nylon 101	900	5°-10°	0°	0°	10°	12°	8°	1°-2°	0°-5° Neg.	15°	45°	1/2°-1°	High Speed M-2
Nylatron® GS	750	5°-10°	0°	0°	10°	12°	8°	1°-2°	0°-5° Neg.	15°	30°	1/2°-1°	Carbide C-2
MC® Nylon-GSM	650	5°-10°	0°	0°	10°	12°	8°	2°-3°	0°-5° Neg.	15°	30°	1/2°-1°	Carbide C-2
Other nylons	500-750	10°-20°	0°	0°	15°-20°	12°	8°	2°-3°	0°-5° Neg.	15°-20°	45°	1°-2°	High Speed M-2
Teflon PTFE	750	10°	0°	0°	15°	12°	8°	2°	0°	15°-20°	45°	1°-2°	C-2/HSS T-15
Fluorosint®	500	10°	0°	0°	15°	12°	8°	2°	0°	15°	30°	1°	Carbide C-2

These figures are provided as a good "starting place" for machining Cadco® Engineering Plastics.

Fig. 9-29 Plastic machining guidelines. Source: Cadillac Plastics, Troy, MI

when the temperature reaches the softening point. The use of coolants, such as mist spray, water-soluble oil, or light cutting oil, is recommended in high speed and automatic operations. A small amount of liquid soap added to water makes an inexpensive but effective coolant.

Fast tool speed and slow material feed is the general machining recommendation. See Table 9-1. A materials selection chart is illustrated in Table 9-2.

The decorating and finishing of plastic parts has a significant impact on both the quality and the cost of the finished product. Each plastic part design must be reviewed to be sure that all aspects of the end-use application, the plastic material, and the manufacturing process have been considered.

A comparison chart (Table 9-3) provides a quick overview of the key plastic decorating techniques.

Table 9-1 Plastic Machining Guidelines

	Sawing (Circular)	Sawing (Band)	Lathe (Turn)	Lathe (Cutoff)	Drilling	Milling	Reaming
Acetals							
Speed (sfpm):	4,000 to 6,000	600 to 2,000	450 to 600	600	300 to 600	1,000 to 3,000	350 to 450
Feed (in./rev.):	Fast, smooth	Fast, smooth	0.0045 to 0.010	0.003 to 0.004	0.004 to 0.015	0.004 to 0.016	0.0055 to 0.015
Tool:	HSS, carbide	HSS	HSS, carbide	HSS, carbide	HSS, carbide	HSS, carbide	HSS, carbide
Clearance (deg):	20 to 30		10 to 25	10 to 25	10 to 25	10 to 20	
Rake (deg):	0	0 to 15 (positive)	0 to 5	0 to 15 (positive)	0 to 10 (positive)	0 to 5 (negative)	0 to 10 (positive)
Set:	Slight	Slight					
Point Angle (deg):					90 to 118		
Cooling:	Dry, air jet, vapor	Dry, air jet	Dry, air jet, vapor	Dry, air jet, vapor	Dry, air jet, vapor	Dry, air jet, vapor	Dry, air jet, vapor
Acrylics							
Speed (sfpm):	8,000 to 12,000	8,000 to 12,000	300 to 600	450 to 500	200 to 400	300 to 600	250 to 400
Feed (in./rev.):	Fast, smooth	Fast, smooth	0.003 to 0.008	0.003 to 0.004	Slow, steady	0.003 to 0.010	0.006 to 0.012
Tool:	HSS, carbide	HSS	HSS, carbide	HSS, carbide	HSS, carbide	HSS, carbide	HSS, carbide
Clearance (deg.):	10 to 20		10 to 20	10 to 20	12 to 15	15	
Rake (deg.):	0 to 10 (positive)	0 to 10 (positive)	0 to 5	0 to 15 (negative)	0 to 5 (negative)	0 to 5 (negative)	0 to 10 (negative)
Set:	Slight	Slight					
Point Angle (deg.):					118		
Cooling:	Dry, air jet, vapor	Dry, air jet, vapor	Dry, air jet, vapor	Dry, air jet, water solution	Dry, air jet, vapor	Dry, air jet, vapor	Dry, air jet, vapor
Fluorocarbons (Teflon)							
Speed (sfpm):	8,000 to 12,000	5,000 to 7,000	400 to 700	425 to 475	200 to 500	1,000 to 3,000	300 to 600
Feed (in./rev.):	Fast, smooth	Fast, smooth	0.002 to 0.010	0.003 to 0.004	0.002 to 0.010	0.004 to 0.016	0.006 to 0.015
Tool:	HSS, carbide	HSS	HSS, carbide	HSS, carbide	HSS, carbide	HSS, carbide	HSS, carbide
Clearance (deg.):	20 to 30		15 to 30	10 to 25	20	7 to 15	10 to 20
Rake (deg.):	0 to 5 (positive)	0 to 10 (positive)	0 to 5	3 to 15 (positive)	0 to 10 (negative)	3 to 15 (positive)	0 to 10 (negative)
Set:	Heavy	Heavy					
Point Angle (deg.):					90 to 118		
Cooling:	Dry, air jet, vapor	Dry, air jet	Dry, air jet, vapor	Dry, air jet, vapor	Dry, air jet, vapor	Dry, air jet, vapor	Dry, air jet, vapor

(continued)

Table 9-1 Plastic Machining Guidelines (continued)

	Sawing (Circular)	Sawing (Band)	Lathe (Turn)	Lathe (Cutoff)	Drilling	Milling	Reaming
Nylons							
Speed (sfpm):	4,000 to 6,000	4,000 to 6,000	500 to 700	700	180 to 450	1,000 to 3,000	300 to 450
Feed (in./rev.):	Fast, smooth	Fast, smooth	0.002 to 0.016	0.002 to 0.016	0.004 to 0.015	0.004 to 0.016	0.005 to 0.015
Tool:	HSS, carbide	HSS	HSS, carbide	HSS, carbide	HSS, carbide	HSS, carbide	HSS, carbide
Clearance (deg.):	20 to 30		5 to 10	7 to 15	10 to 15	7 to 15,	
Rake (deg.):	15 (positive)	0 to 15 (positive)	0 to 5	0 to 5 (positive)	0 to 5 (positive)	0 to 5 (negative)	0 to 10 (positive)
Set:	Slight	Slight					
Point Angle (deg.):					90 to 110 under 1/2" 118 over 1/2"		
Cooling:	Dry, air jet, vapor	Dry, air jet	Dry, air jet, vapor	Dry, air jet, vapor	Dry, air jet, vapor	Dry, air jet, vapor	Dry, air jet, vapor
Polyolefins (UHMW)							
Speed (sfpm):	1,650 to 5,000	3,900 to 5,000	600 to 800	425 to 475	200 to 600	1,000 to 3,000	280 to 600
Feed (in./rev.):	Fast, smooth	Fast, smooth	0.0015 to 0.025	0.003 to 0.004	0.004 to 0.020	0.06 to 0.020	0.006 to 0.012
Tool:	HSS, carbide	HSS, carbide	HSS, carbide	HSS, carbide	HSS, carbide	HSS, carbide	HSS, carbide
Clearance (deg.)	15		15 to 25	15 to 25	10 to 20	10 to 20	10 to 20
Rake (deg.)	0 to 8 (positive)	0 to 10 (positive)	0 to 15	3 to 15 (positive)	0 to 5 (positive)	0 to 10 (positive)	0 to 10 (negative)
Set:	Heavy	Heavy					
Point Angle (deg.)					90 to 118		
Cooling	Dry, air jet, vapor	Dry, air jet, vapor	Dry, air jet, vapor	Dry, air jet, vapor	Dry, air jet, vapor	Dry, air jet, vapor	Dry, air jet, vapor

This information is designed as a guideline and is not to be construed as absolute. Because of the variety of work and diversity of finishes required, it may be necessary to depart from the suggestions in the table. A good practice to follow is to run a test workpiece before starting a production run. Source: Cadillac Plastic & Chemical Co., Troy, MI

Table 9-2 Materials Selection Chart—Plastic Properties

Property	Units	Test method ASTM	Acetal	Cast acrylic	Cast nylon	Nylatron® NSM	6/6 Nylon	Nylatron® GS	Teflon	Fluorosint® 500 PTFE	UHMW
Mechanical											
Specific gravity	g/cm°	D-792	1.41-1.42	1.17-1.2	1.15-1.17	1.13	1.13	1.14-1.18	2.1-2.3	2.25-2.35	0.94
Ultimate tensile strength, @ 73 °F	psi	D-638	8,800-12,000	8,000	11,000-14,000	9,400	9,400	10,000-14,000	1,500-5,000	750-1,200	6,000
Elongation, @ 73 °F	%	D-638	12-75	2.0	10-60	50	50	5-150	75-350	1-10	300
Compressive @ 10% deflection-strength	psi	D-695	16,000-18,000	11,000-19,000	—	—	12,000	12,000-13,000	—	—	—
Tensile modulus of elasticity, 73 °F	psi	D-638	410,000-520,000	350,000-500,000	350,000-450,000	320,000	320,000	450,000-500,000	50,000-90,000	375,000-600,000	—
Tensile impact strength @ 73 °F	ft/lb/in²	D-1122	40-90		80-130	90	90-180	50-180	No break		400
Flexural strength, @ 73 °F	psi	D-790	13,000-15,500	12,000	16,000-17,500	14,000	12,500-14,000	16,000-18,000		1,500-2,500	
Flexural modulus of elasticity, @ 73 °F	psi	D-790	375,000-550,000	350,000-500,000		350,000	175,000-410,000	400,000-500,000	525,000-650,000	110,000	77,000
Shear strength	psi	D-732	7,700-9,500		10,500-11,500	10,000	9,600	9,500-10,200	90,000-110,000		4,000
Coefficient of friction (dry vs. steel) dynamic			0.15-0.35		0.16-0.25	0.13-0.16	0.17-0.43	0.15-0.35	0.04-0.10	0.1-0.2	0.15-0.20
Hardness: Rockwell (R), 73 °F		D-785	R119-122	M80-M100	R112-120	108	R110-120	R110-125	10-20	R45-65	52
Hardness: Durometer (D) 73 °F		D-676	78-94 (ASTM-785)	78-94 (ASTM-785)		86	D80-85	D80-90	55-70	D64-47	70
Thermal											
Continuous service temperature in Air (Max.)	°F		180	150	200-225	180-200	180-200	180-200	—	500	200
Deformation under load 2,000 psi, @ 122 °F	%	D-621	0.3-1.0		0.5-1.0	0.90	1.0-3.0	0.5-2.5	9-11	0.8-1.1	—
Heat deflection: 264 psi	°F	D-648	220-255		200-425	200	200-450	200-470	100-140	240-300	174

(continued)

Table 9-2 Materials Selection Chart—Plastic Properties

Property	Units	Test method ASTM	Acetal	Cast acrylic	Cast nylon	Nylatron® NSM	6/6 Nylon	Nylatron® GS	Teflon	Fluorosint® 500 PTFE	UHMW
Heat deflection: 66 psi	°F	D-648	316-338	—	400-425	—	400-460	400-490	—	—	115
Coefficient of linear thermal expansion (in/in/°F x 10^{-5}); −86°F to 86°F	in/in/°F	D-696	4.2-4.7	3.5	5.0	5.0	5.5	3.5	5.5-7.5	1.25-1.50×10^{-5}	—
Melting point	°F	D-789	329-347	—	430±10	430±10	482-500	482-500	621±9	621±	NA
Electrical											
Dielectric strength, short time, in air @ 73°F	kv/cm v/mil	D-1945	380-500	400	500-600	—	300-400	300-400	500-650	275-300	900
Volume resistivity @ 73°F	OHM-CM	D-257	1×10^{14} – 1×10^{15}	10^{15}	—	—	4.5×10^{13}	2.5×10^{13}	10^{15}	$>10^{13}$	$>10^{18}$
Dielectric constant: 60C 60Hz	—	D-150	3.7	3.5-4.5	3.7	—	4.1	—	2.0-2.1	2.85-3.65	2.3-2.35
Dielectric constant: 10^{-3}C 10Hz	—	D-150	3.7	3.0-3.5	3.7	—	4.0	—	2.0-2.1	2.9-3.6	2.3-2.35
Dielectric contact: 10^6C 10^6Hz	—	—	3.7	3.0	3.7	—	3.4	—	2.0-2.1	2.9-3.6	2.3-2.35
Water absorption 24 hrs. immersion	%	D-570	0.12-0.25	0.4	0.12-0.25	1.2	0.6-1.5	0.5-1.4	<0.01	<0.01	NIL
Saturation	%	D-570	0.80-0.90	—	0.80-0.90	5.3	7-9	6-8	—	—	NIL

(1) 0.080" thick, (2) Specimen 1/8" thick, 2" diameter, (3) 0.040" thick, (4) ASTM D-1457 used for thin specimens. Courtesy of Cadillac Plastic & Chemical Co., Troy, MI

Table 9-3 Comparison of the Four Most Common Decorating Methods

	Direct screen printing	Pad printing	Hot stamping	Heat transfer
Recognition factors	Thicker and more opaque, no clear or adhesive at edges	Thinner and less opaque fine copy; large color areas may look weak	Colors usually debossed, can be bright gold or silver	May have tooling halo around design, usually multicolor
Image size and limitations	Screens can be made any size	7 by 14 inches usual limit, special machines can print 10 by 20 inches	Limited by pressure of machine and tendency to trap air, usual range 300 to 500 psi; roll-on solves air entrapment and can apply 12 by 24 inches	Limited by pressure of machine and tendency to trap air, usual range 100 to 300 psi (soft goods as low as 30 to 50 psi); roll-on solves air entrapment and can apply 12 by 24 inches
Resolution of detail	Medium	Fine to medium	Medium	Fine—including 133-line four-color process
Large areas of solid color	OK with good equipment and operator	Not good without multiple prints of color	Possible, but trapped air can be a problem; roll-on machine will help	Possible, but trapped air can be a problem; roll-on machine will help
Opacity	Good	Poor; with multiple prints only fair	Good	Good if screen printed; fair if gravure printed
Color match	Your responsibility in-house or ordered from outside supplier	Your responsibility in-house or ordered from outside supplier	Use closest color of foil available, or for long runs get it custom formulated	Inks have to be custom formulated anyway when transfer is printed
Registration of colors if multicolored	Fair to good depending on equipment, tooling, operator, and size stability of plastic from first to last print	Fair to very good depending on equipment and whether part stays in same nest throughall color prints and on quality of the tooling	Fair to good depending on equipment, tooling, and size stability of plastic	Very good; four-color process, 133-line screen demands tight registration; so does multicolor and fine detail
Part shape and limitations	Flat or single curve (cylinder)	Can be irregular or compound curve but art distortion requires trial and error to correct	Flat or simple curve (cylinder)	Flat, single curve, or slight compound curve; carrier-paper wrinkling limits shape and size on compound curves

(continued)

Table 9-3 Comparison of the Four Most Common Decorating Methods (continued)

	Direct screen printing	Pad printing	Hot stamping	Heat transfer
Arc limits on cylinder or a cylinder with draft or taper 1° or less	Almost 360°, avoiding ink-to-screen contact on the wrap if it will be a problem	Approximately 100° arc for reciprocal machine or 360° for special wrap machines	Approximately 90° arc for reciprocal machine; 360° (with slight overlap preferred) for wrap machines	Approximately 90° arc for reciprocal machine; 360° with slight overlap preferred for wrap machine except if wax release; then 360° minus (⅛ inch)
Process wet ink or dry	Wet—drying or curing required between and/or after final color	Wet—drying or curing required between and/or after final color; some ink systems can be printed "wet on wet"	Dry—proceed to next process	Dry—proceed to next process
Inventory required	Screens of various meshes; inks to make custom colors for particular substrate chemistry; solvents, cleaners, retarders, squeegees, or order match color inks as needed	Pads of various sizes, shapes, and durometers; inks to make custom colors for particular substrate chemistries; solvents, cleaners, retarders, or order match colors as needed	Various hot-stamping foils in various colors of chemistries compatible with surfaces to be marked; or order as needed	Heat transfers for a specific job
EPA and fire-safety considerations	Flammable materials must be stored and insured accordingly	Flammable materials must be stored and insured accordingly	None	None
Learning-curve time frame for system startup	Days to weeks	Days to weeks	Hours to days	Hours to days
New operator learning-curve time frame	Hours to days	Hours to days	Minutes to hours	Minutes to hours
Setup skill level	Skilled	Skilled	Semiskilled	Semiskilled
Operator skill level	Semiskilled	Semiskilled	Unskilled	Unskilled
Part changeover, new part, new design	Minutes to hours to change tooling (nest), change screens, change inks, reregister (longer for multicolor)	Minutes to hours to change tooling (nest), change cliches, change pads, change inks, reregister (longer for multicolor)	Seconds to minutes (rarely hours) to change tooling (nest), change application head, change foil, reregister (longer for multicolor), recheck pressure, dwell, and temperature	Seconds to minutes (rarely hours) to change tooling (nest), change application head, change roll of heat transfers, reregister (time same as for single color), recheck pressure, dwell, and temperature

(continued)

Table 9-3 Comparison of the Four Most Common Decorating Methods (continued)

	Direct screen printing	Pad printing	Hot stamping	Heat transfer
Process variance causing defective print	Ink viscosity somewhat critical	Ink viscosity extremely critical	Process is quite stable; silicone rubber die "forgives" mild surface blemishes	Process is quite stable since less pressure is required; softer rubber (50 to 60 durometer) "forgives" many surface blemishes
Part variance causing defective print	Poor surface finish and such blemishes as sink marks (some defects)	Surface blemishes usually unaffected unless blemish is extreme (least defects)	Direct ram overcomes thickness changes; toggle machines very sensitive to thickness changes (some defects)	Direct ram overcomes thickness changes; toggle machines very sensitive to thickness changes (some defects)
Cost of equipment	Small to large area (100 in²) not very cost sensitive but very cost sensitive to multicolor	Small to large area cost sensitive; cost sensitive also to multicolor	Small to large area cost sensitive (multicolor more than one pass or more than one machine)	Cost sensitive to size; not sensitive to multicolor tooling (nest and heads); cost same for one or multicolor
Cost of tooling	Low to moderate for single color, moderate to high depending on tolerances required for multicolor	Low to moderate for single color, moderate to high depending on tolerances required for multicolor	Low to moderate for single color, moderate to high depending on tolerances required for multicolor	Low to moderate cost as for single color even though graphics may be multicolor
Part input/output equipment cost	Approximately same for all processes but may be more costly for multicolor	Approximately same for all processes but may be more costly for multicolor	Approximately same for all processes but may be more costly for multicolor	Approximately same for all processes but is not more costly for multicolor
Cost of inks, foil, transfers	Inks—not very cost sensitive to size	Inks—not very cost sensitive to size	Foils—cost sensitive to size; costs for multicolor increase linearly per color and area	Transfers—cost sensitive to size, not as sensitive to additional colors

Source: Meyercord Co., Carol Stream, IL

10

Assembly of Plastic Parts

Most plastic parts are attached, in some manner, with other plastic or nonplastic parts to form an assembly. The methods used to create this attachment are varied and often not clearly understood by product designers and plastic product manufacturers.

Plastic material offers the widest range of assembly techniques when compared with those used for metals, wood, ceramic, and paper; however, the most benefit will be gained when the assembly of the product(s) is considered early in the plastic product design process.

It is also important that the designer does not attempt to force an assembly technique on a plastic product when it was intended for another material. Plastics should be considered unique.

Finally, the assembly process should maximize the functionality of the plastic material and the design. The assembly techniques discussed in this chapter include:

- Bonding—solvent, adhesive, induction, and tapes
- Welding—spin, vibration, hot gas, fusion, ultrasonic, and dielectric
- Joining—mechanical fasteners, heat staking, ultrasonic inserting, and snap fits

Bonding

Bonding is an assembly process in which two or more plastic parts are held together by the action of a third material. The third material may be a solvent, an adhesive, or an induction-activated compound.

Solvent Bonding

Solvent bonding is one of the simplest methods of assembling thermoplastic parts. It is also one assembly method that many of us are exposed to at an early age, *e.g.*, building plastic (polystyrene) models using a solvent cement (acetone or toluene).

The first requirement that must be met when attempting to solvent bond two plastics together is that there must be a chemical/solvent available that will mildly dissolve the plastic. Meeting this requirement is difficult to impossible with several plastics, including: polyolefins (polyethylene and polypropylene), polyamides (nylons), polyacetals, polytetrafluoroethylenes (Teflon), and most thermosetting plastics.

Plastic materials that are excellent candidates for solvent bonding include: styrenics (polystyrene, ABS, SAN), vinyls (PVC), acrylics, and polycarbonate.

During the solvent bonding of these materials, care must be taken not to apply excess solvent, which may degrade the plastic by "crazing" or cracking its surface beyond the location where bonding is desired.

How It Works. When a solvent is applied to the surface of a plastic, the solvent dissolves some of the polymer. The polymer becomes "plasticized," or softened, allowing the polymer molecules to move. When two plastic surfaces are prepared with a solvent and then pressed together, the polymer molecules at the two surfaces are able to move across the interface of the surfaces and intertwine with the polymer molecules of the other surface.

When the solvent evaporates, those molecules that wandered across the interface will be frozen or locked into place, thus creating a bond between the two materials. See Fig. 10-1.

To effect a good bond, the two plastic materials should be identical, *e.g.*, PVC to PVC. It is possible to bond plastics of the same family, such as ABS and polystyrene, because they are both styrenics.

The solvents commonly used are:

- Acetone
- Methylene chloride
- Toluene
- Styrene
- Methyl ethyl ketone (MEK)

Care should be taken when solvent bonding plastic materials because the vapors from these solvents are dangerous.

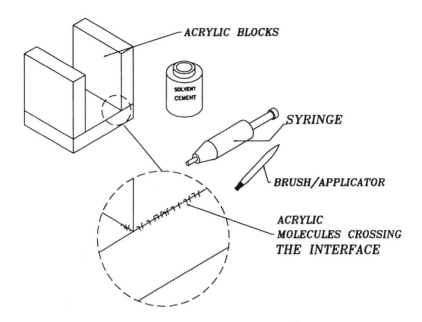

Fig. 10-1 Solvent bonding

Typical solvent bonding applications include:

- Joining PVC pipe and conduit
- Joining PVC flooring materials
- Assembly of styrenic components

The application of the solvent to the joint area needs to be accurate and controlled. This can be accomplished by using a brush or a syringe-type applicator.

Once the solvent is applied to the joint, the plastic surfaces will soften and become tacky. The areas being joined must have continuous pressure applied to provide a strong bond.

Once the solvent has "flashed off," or evaporated, the resulting joint will be a strong cohesive bond that is as strong as the base material itself.

If a heavier bodied or more viscous solvent bonding medium is required, the base plastic to be bonded can be dissolved in the solvent. There should be a greater amount of solvent than base material for best results. This thicker solvent system will be useful in joining two materials that may have small gaps in the joint area.

Adhesive Bonding

Adhesive bonding involves joining two or more materials, plastic or non-plastic, with a third material, an adhesive. When selecting adhesives, one must consider: loads, environment, substrates, application technique, and cost. The adhesive must have characteristics that are compatible with all the materials being joined.

Ability to Bond. Structural adhesives used in manufacturing processes today are comparable to other forms of joining materials. For example, two pieces of sheet metal normally are candidates for welding that joins the metal with a force equal to ~3000 to 3500 psi tensile strength. Polymeric adhesives can easily exceed this bond strength with ranges of 4000 to 6000 psi available.

Resistance to Degradation. Structural adhesives are not susceptible to galvanic action, which will degrade welded metal joints. Note that adhesive selection should be thorough in the consideration of the environmental exposure because many otherwise strong adhesives are weakened by exposure to ultraviolet radiation (sunlight), moisture, or solvents.

Ease of Application. Application of adhesive systems has historically been difficult and is one of the main reasons that the use of adhesives has not been considered for high-production applications. Recent advances in both adhesive materials and application equipment have made structural adhesives viable assembly processes in production environments.

Another consideration that makes polymeric adhesives attractive for product assembly is their ability to conform to the surfaces to which they are bonding without distortion of any of the surfaces. The adhesive can also act as a sealant, protecting the products from the introduction of foreign fluids.

Cost. The material cost of adhesives on a weight-to-weight basis is more expensive than conventional assembly systems (mechanical fasteners/welding); however, the downstream costs, such as equipment, durability, reliability, and quality, can easily outweigh any initial cost issues.

The product designer must consider the total cost to manufacture the product prior to selecting the assembly systems.

Many manufacturers do not consider adhesives to be part of the material cost of a product; instead, adhesives are often considered to be overhead cost items. This may not provide the cost visibility necessary to determine the cost effectiveness of adhesive assembly.

Shelf life and Pot life. When selecting an adhesive system, some hidden costs may not be initially apparent to the designer and manufacturer. Two of the largest potential costs are involved with the shelf life and the pot life of the materials.

Shelf life is the time adhesive systems, including their components, can be inventoried and still be considered usable. Those factors that negatively affect shelf life include:

- Storage at too high temperature
- Storage in high humidity or direct sunlight
- Storage in open containers

Pot life is the time a manufacturer has to use the adhesive once all the components are mixed. The pot life of the adhesive and the production rate of the equipment need to be balanced to prevent unnecessary waste. Those factors that negatively affect pot life in addition to those that affect shelf life include:

- Process delays or changes in production rates
- Contaminated adhesive components
- Poorly mixed adhesive components

Adhesives are often thought to be glues, but they are not. Although the verb "to glue" is applicable to both glues and adhesives, glues are made from natural materials, whereas adhesives are man-made and are often polymers themselves. Examples of some glues are: fish oil-based glues and animal-based glues.

Structural adhesives are hot-melt, anaerobics, epoxies, cyanoacrylates, and polyolefins.

Anaerobics are one-part adhesive systems that cure in the absence of oxygen and in the presence of an active surface such as metal. The most common application of anaerobic adhesive is in the thread locking area.

Epoxies are two-part structural adhesives that are used in bonding, coating, and encapsulation applications. Epoxies are very durable and provide high tensile strength.

Cyanoacrylates are onr-part adhesive systems that were developed for the space and nuclear industries, but they have also been successfully marketed in consumer applications as "super glues." Cyanoacrylates can bond several forms of substrates and are excellent for short-term bonding and positioning of components for later assembly. The limitations of cyanoacrylates are their limited temperature range (<100 °F) and poor resistance to moisture. Since no single adhesive will bond to all types of plastics, several different types of adhesive systems and forms are available.

Adhesive formats include:

- Powders
- Liquids
- Pastes
- Mastics
- Tapes
- Films

Additionally, adhesives are classified into common groups: solvent cements, bodied adhesives, and monomeric chemicals.

Solvent cements are used for a limited number of thermoplastic materials and require that the plastic being bonded can be dissolved by the solvent.

Bodied adhesives are sometimes called "dope" adhesives. The adhesive is a solvent that contains small quantities of the base plastic.

Monomeric cements are made from the same resin as the parent plastic. The monomeric cement is activated by a catalyst. The bonding occurs by polymerization and not by solvent evaporation.

Elastomeric adhesives are adhesives that will stretch their bond to at least twice the original bond thickness without negatively affecting bond strength. This rubber-like property provides excellent adhesion to rubber and elastomeric materials and excellent shock and impact resistance.

Reactive adhesives are thermosetting materials, such as epoxy, and they are especially effective when bonding two thermosetting plastics together. Reactive adhesives usually have two components, a resin and a hardener. They are one of the key adhesives used in the manufacturing and assembly of composite plastic products.

Adhesive systems are also characterized as either cold setting or hot setting. A cold setting adhesive will cure at temperatures below 20 °C. A hot setting adhesive will cure only if exposed to temperatures above 100 °C.

Induction Bonding

Induction bonding is a unique assembly process that lends itself to plastic product assembly. The principle is quite simple—an induced electric field is generated in proximity to a plastic part that is to be bonded to either metal or another plastic substrate. See Fig. 10-2 and 10-3. A special adhesive compound, containing 0.5 to 6% metallic particles, is the bonding agent located between the two adherends. The induced electric field (2 to 6 MHz) will pass through the plastic with no effect, but when the adhesive is exposed to the field, the metallic particles are excited and generate thermal energy. This heat activates

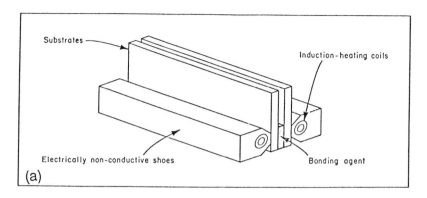

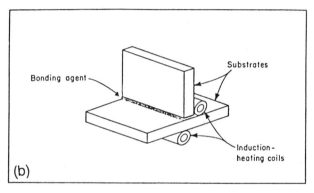

Fig. 10-2 (a) Cross section of basic setup for induction bonding. (b) Induction-heating bonding at a T-joint. The coils are placed diagonally above and below the joint. Source: Hellerbond Technology Company, Columbus, OH

the otherwise dormant adhesive. Pressure is applied to the adherends, and the plastic is now bonded.

One advantage of induction bonding is that the adhesive system can be applied to the plastic part at the convenience of the manufacturer and activated at the convenience of the assembler. Another advantage is that the adhesive system can be made of the same resin as the plastic to be joined. Again, the presence of the metallic particle is required to effect the melting process, but because the same plastic is used, materials such as polyolefins and nylons can be bonded.

Tapes

Adhesive-backed tapes have developed into a sophisticated and technically feasible means of bonding plastic parts to each other and to other substrates.

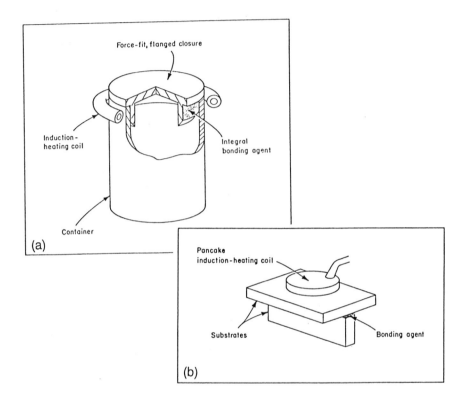

Fig. 10-3 (a) Integral bonding. Closure containing bonding agent is force-fit into container, and the two are subsequently bonded. (b) The pancake induction-heating coil is used when access to both sides of the bonding agent is unavailable. Source: Heller-bond Technology Company, Columbus, OH

One major advantage of pressure-sensitive tapes is that they can be pre-shaped or die cut to fit the geometry of the part(s) to be joined. This preshaping greatly facilitates the manufacturing assembly process and reduces waste.

Pressure-sensitive tapes are available in a wide variety of formats, including foam tapes. The foam tape systems provide bonding and insulation (thermal, electrical, and sound). Foam tape systems can also act as expansion/compression areas for assemblies that may be susceptible to wide ranges in temperature and coefficients of thermal expansion.

Fig. 10-4 Precut tape adhesives. Source: Stik-II Division of the October Company, Inc., Easthampton, MA

Tapes are available in rolls, sheets, spools, and die cut shapes. See Fig. 10-4 and 10-5.

Welding of Plastics

Spin Welding

Spin welding is an assembly process that requires no special adhesives and utilizes very simple equipment. Mostly used for joining round or cylindrical thermoplastic parts, spin welding has found a niche in the assembly of nylon fuel filters and insulated beverage containers.

The two circular halves to be assembled are located above one another and either spun in opposite directions, or one half is set spinning while the other is fixtured to remain stationary. See Fig. 10-6. The two halves are brought sufficiently close to each other using only enough pressure to generate friction at the interface of the two parts. The friction will quickly melt the plastic, forming a thin film of plastic melt. At this stage in the process, the rotation ceases, and additional pressure is applied to force the two halves together using the film of plastic melt as the bonding medium. The parts are held together long enough for the melt to cool and secure the assembly.

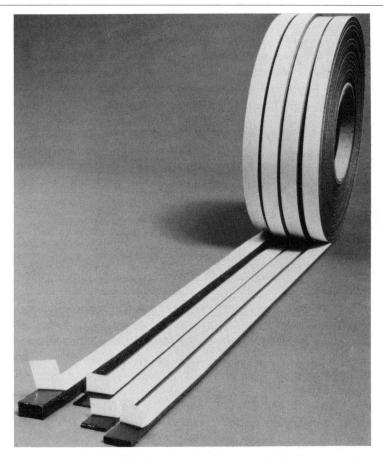

Fig. 10-5 Double-sided tape rolls. Source: Stik-II Division of the October Company, Inc., Easthampton, MA

One major quality concern that occurs when spin welding two thermoplastic parts together is the generation of weld flash caused as a result of squeezing the melt. Special joint designs should be used to trap any joint flash; otherwise, the flash will have to be removed in a secondary operation.

The spin welding process provides a strong bond and acts as a hermetic, or environmentally tight, seal.

A variation of the spin welding process is spin swagging. In this process, a neutral material (Teflon) that will not melt or stick, is inserted into a chuck that

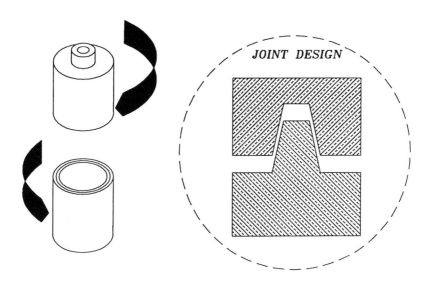

Fig. 10-6 Spin welding—A simple, low-cost assembly technique

will spin at 2500 to 5000 rpm. The plastic part to be assembled is designed to be a boss of part A that is inserted through part B, as shown in Fig. 10-7. The spinning tool is allowed to come in contact with the boss, and, as in the spin welding of two parts, the frictional heat will soften the plastic boss. Then additional pressure forms a bradlike head securing the two parts together.

Vibration Welding

Vibration welding was developed to serve the assembly needs of larger—up to 22 in. (550 mm) long and 16 in. (400 mm) wide—irregularly shaped thermoplastic parts without the use of solvents or adhesives. See Fig. 10-8.

Vibration welding uses the frictional heat generated when the two parts to be assembled are held together with a light pressure and caused to slide or rub against each other over a small displacement—0.040 to 0.160 in. (1 to 4 mm)—at relatively low frequencies—120 to 240 Hz. To accomplish this assembly process, special vibration welding equipment is required since the uniformity of the bond and the accurate positioning of the two parts is critical.

Most thermoplastic materials can be vibration welded whether they are processed using injection molding, extrusion, thermoforming, or foam molding processes.

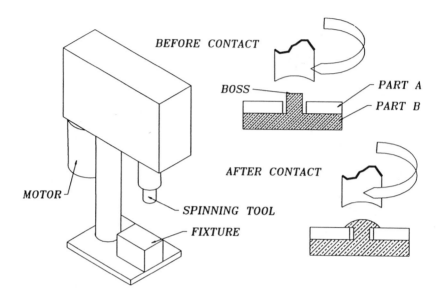

Fig. 10-7 Spin welder

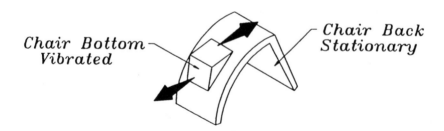

Fig. 10-8 Vibration welding. Frictional heat bonds parts

Vibration welding is particularly useful with the semicrystalline plastics such as polyethylene, polypropylene, acetals, and nylons. These materials are not readily bondable using conventional techniques, such as adhesive bonding.

Vibration Welding Equipment. The vibration welder employs a simple vibrator mechanism consisting of only one moving element with no bearing

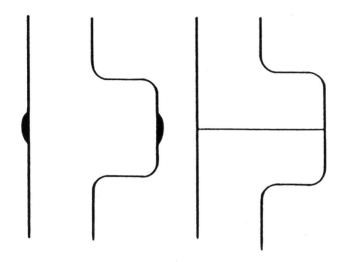

Fig. 10-9 Butt joint for vibration welding

surfaces. The reciprocating motion is achieved by a magnetic force alternating at 120 to 240 Hz that acts directly on the mechanical suspension.

The vibrating element engages and holds the plastic part to be vibrated, while the stationary element holds the other part of the assembly. Pressure is applied to the parts by a pneumatic clamping mechanism that engages the stationary element or tray, locking it to the vibrating element during the welding cycle.

The fixturing for vibration welding is usually simple and inexpensive, consisting of aluminum plates with cutouts that conform to the geometry of the parts being assembled.

It is possible to vibration weld more than two parts at one time by using a multiple-cavity fixture.

Special Design Considerations. Two of the most important design considerations for plastic parts to be vibration welded together are: (a) parts must be free to vibrate relative to one another in the plane of the joint, and (b) joint area must be supported during welding.

Several vibration welding joint designs are available to the plastic part designer. The butt joint is the simplest and is illustrated in Fig. 10-9.

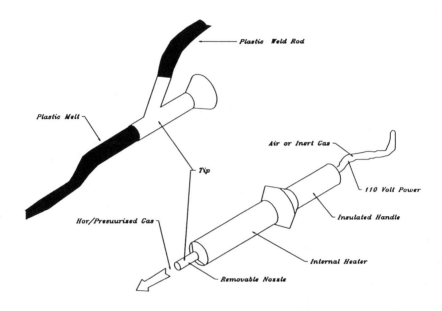

Fig. 10-10 Hot gas welding. Sheets of plastic are webbed together with a bond strength greater than the strength of the plastic itself

Hot Gas Welding

Hot gas welding of plastics is a variation of metal welding techniques. The hot gas welding apparatus is quite simple (see Fig. 10-10), consisting of a "gun" that acts as a source of hot air or inert gas.

The hot gas welding system is frequently used to assemble and seal sheets of polypropylene in the fabrication of large chemical tanks. To accomplish the welding, the joint areas of the tank are designed to fit together while providing an area to add a bead of plastic melt, which acts as both adhesive and sealant. The hot gas welder is brought up to temperature, and air is allowed to pass over the heating elements, creating a focused point of hot air. A weld rod made of the same plastic as the material to be joined is presented in front of the hot air stream and is allowed to melt and fit into the joint area. As the welding process continues, the bead is pulled in front of the hot air, thus allowing for a continuous process.

Recent advances in hot melt technology have resulted in the addition of pressure to the welding system, which provides a more uniform and consistent weld joint.

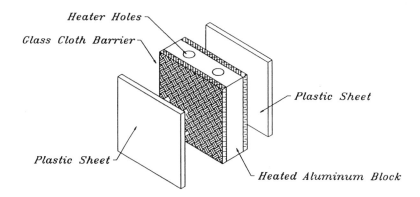

Fig. 10-11 Fusion bonding equipment

Fusion Welding

Fusion welding is the process of heating two plastic surfaces and joining them by applying pressure to the joint. The equipment involved in fusion bonding is simple and usually custom manufactured. It consists of an aluminum plate that has heating elements housed within its center. On the outside of the metal plate, glass cloth is bonded to provide a slippery and nonstick surface. See Fig. 10-11.

The two plastic surfaces to be joined are pressed on either side of the heated metal plate. After a sufficient amount of time (enough to soften the plastic surfaces) the two plastic parts are taken off the heated metal tool and pressed together long enough to cool and join the two parts.

Fusion bonding is primarily used to join thermoplastic parts that have large flat surface areas.

Ultrasonic Welding

Ultrasonic welding of plastic parts is unique and one of the most efficient assembling processes available.

Ultrasonic assembly of plastic is often mistaken to be assembly by the application of sound waves, but actually ultrasonic welding is accomplished by the heat generated via the friction resulting from high-frequency mechanical vibrations.

Ultrasonic actually means "beyond hearing." The human ear can hear sounds with frequencies as high as ~18 kHz. The frequency of the mechanical vibrations in the ultrasonic welding process is either 20 or 40 kHz, far beyond human hearing limits.

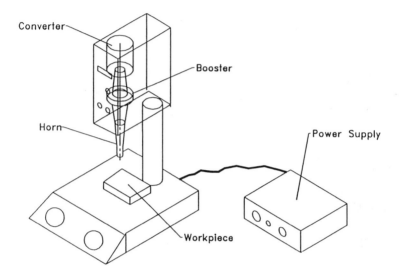

Fig. 10-12 Ultrasonic welder components

The process involved in ultrasonic welding is as follows:

1. An ultrasonic vibration is focused on a specially designed joint be-
    tween two plastic parts to be welded.
2. The ultrasonic vibration at the joint generates frictional heat, which
    melts the plastic.
3. Additional pressure is applied to the melted plastic in the joint area,
    and the two plastic parts are bonded.

Variations of the above process can be used to join two similar plastic parts,
install metal inserts into plastic parts, and trim or degate plastic parts.

Equipment. The ultrasonic processing equipment consists of four distinct
elements: power supply, converter, booster, and horn. See Fig. 10-12 and 10-13.

The power supply converts incoming power (60 Hz alternating current)
into high-frequency (20 to 40 kHz) electrical power.

The converter uses a piezoelectric element to convert the electrical energy
into a mechanical vibration.

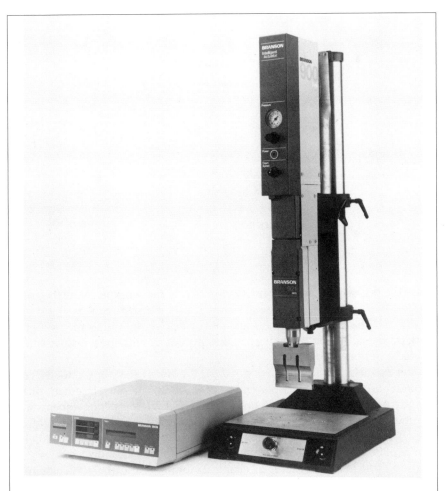

Fig. 10-13 Ultrasonic equipment and power supply. Source: Branson Ultrasonics Corporation, Danbury, CT

The booster or booster horn is an impedance or amplitude transformer that either increases or decreases the amplitude of the ultrasonic frequency to match the horn used in any specific application. The booster is one-half wavelength long.

The horn, like the booster, is also one-half wavelength long, and must be made of a resonant material such as titanium or aluminum. The horn com-

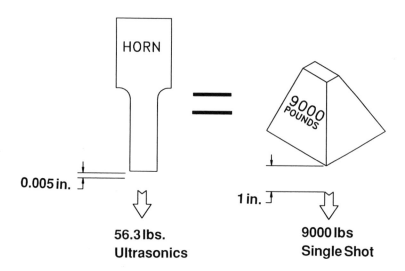

Fig. 10-14 Force equivalent to ultrasonic vibrations

pletes the transfer of the mechanical vibration to the workpiece. As the name implies, the horn, like its musical counterparts, must be tuned. The shape, length, and design of the horn must be correct for the ultrasonic welder to work properly. The tip of the horn comes in contact with the workpiece to be welded and does all the work.

The Process. As shown in Fig. 10-14, the tip of the horn actually goes through an excursion or displacement of 0.005 in. This displacement of the horn tip occurs at the rate of 20 to 40 kHz. This high frequency (mechanical) vibration creates friction within the plastic. The friction generates enough heat to melt a localized area of plastic near the horn and/or workpiece allowing similar plastics to be spot welded or metal inserts to be installed.

In addition to the ultrasonic mechanical vibrations, the ultrasonic assembly equipment allows the horn assembly to move under slight pressure (~40 to 60 psi) to execute the weld or insertion to specified depth. A controlled "stop," or final weld point, is required by the process.

There are several common applications for ultrasonics in plastic product manufacturing, including:

- Direct welding of similar plastics by spot welding
- Direct welding of similar plastics by employing an "energy director"
- Staking of plastic to a substrate of a different material
- Insertion of metal inserts
- Degating

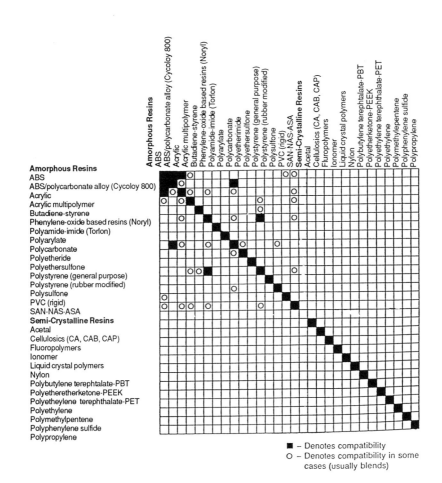

Fig. 10-15 Compatibility of thermoplastics. Source: Branson Ultrasonics Corporation, Danbury, CT

Spot Welding and Direct Welding. Ultrasonic welding of plastics requires that the welded plastics be of the same or similar families. A chart illustrated in Fig. 10-15 shows the compatibility of different materials.

The characteristics of the plastic, *i.e.*, whether it is rigid or soft, amorphous, or crystalline must be considered. Also important to ultrasonic welding is whether or not a plastic melts or transmits energy.

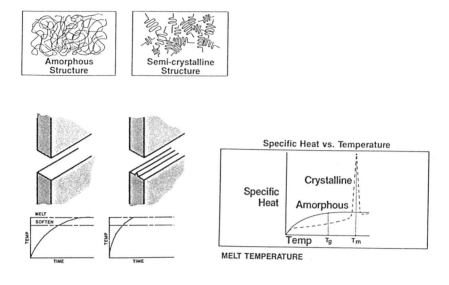

Fig. 10-16 Amorphous and crystalline plastics welded with ultrasonics. Source: Branson Ultrasonics Corporation, Danbury, CT

As discussed in earlier chapters, plastics are either amorphous or semicrystalline in structure. See Fig. 10-16.

Amorphous plastics are excellent candidates for ultrasonic assembly because they require low energy levels. The amorphous, or random, arrangement of the plastic molecules provides the plastic with a broad melting range that allows the material to soften slowly and flow without prematurely hardening.

Ultrasonic energy is easily transmitted through amorphous plastics. Crystalline plastics require a higher energy level, and because of their highly ordered molecular structure, these plastics have a sharp melt point and solidify quickly. The semicrystalline structure allows the ultrasonic vibrations to be absorbed when the plastic is in its solid phase. This results in the higher energy requirements for welding.

Another variable of ultrasonically welding plastic is the proximity of the horn to the joint or point where the weld is desired. It should be remembered that the horn will be in contact with the plastic, but the point where welding occurs may be a distance away from the horn because of material thickness or part design. If the distance between the horn and the desired weld joint is less than 1/4 in. (6 mm), it is considered to be a "near field" weld. If this distance

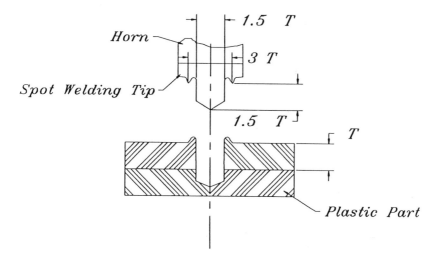

Fig. 10-17 Horn geometry for ultrasonic spot welding

is greater than 1/4 in., it is considered to be a "far field" weld. The further the distance, the more important the energy transmittance ability of the plastic becomes.

Spot welding using ultrasonics requires that the horn tip be shaped in such a manner that the penetration of both plastic surfaces is allowed and that the resulting displacement of plastic be shaped on the part surface. See Fig. 10-17. It is critical that the plastics being spot welded have the same melt range to ensure that there is a good weld.

Spot welding does not require any unique part design feature on the plastic, and spot welding is especially useful on flat surfaces. Spot welding will leave a surface blemish on the part.

Welding of plastic parts with a designed energy director is more common than spot welding in that it allows the assembler to define exactly where the weld will occur without any surface blemish on the surface of the part. The key to this welding technique is the energy director. See Fig. 10-18. While there are several energy director designs, they all have the same objective—to focus the mechanical vibrations that are transmitted through the plastic part and effect a weld at a defined location.

The energy director can be designed to nest and locate two plastic parts in the correct orientation (design for manufacturing) prior to welding.

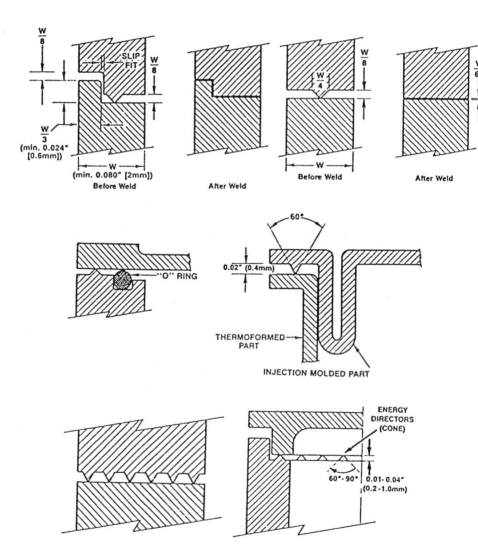

Fig. 10-18 Energy director and joint designs for ultrasonic welding. Source: Branson Ultrasonics Corporation, Danbury, CT

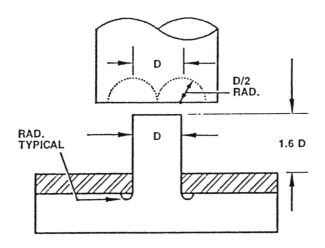

Fig. 10-19 Horn design for staking bosses with ultrasonics. Source: Branson Ultrasonics Corporation, Danbury, CT

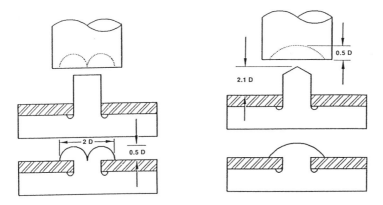

Fig. 10-20 Ultrasonic staking. Source: Branson Ultrasonics Corporation, Danbury, CT

The energy director is the first point to soften and melt when ultrasonic vibrations are applied. The energy director should be located in the same direction as the horn, and it may be desirable to allow for a flash well in the joint design to reduce the risk of having melted plastic exit the joint area.

Ultrasonic staking (see Fig. 10-19 and 10-20) is one method of assembling two different materials. A boss or post is designed to protrude above the

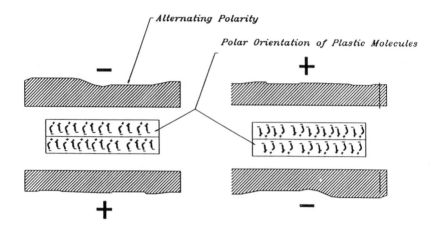

Fig. 10-21 Dielectric sealing

surface of the lower plastic part and through the thickness of the upper part. The ultrasonic horn will brad the post, thus holding the two parts together.

Insertion of Metal Inserts. Ultrasonic vibration assembly can be used to install threaded metal inserts into plastics.

Dielectric Sealing

Some plastics, such as PVC, exhibit a high dielectric loss and thus are candidates for an assembly process called dielectric sealing. This process is commonly used to join plasticized (flexible) PVC films in such applications as inflatable flotation toys, rafts, and waterbed mattresses.

The process uses a high-frequency (27 to 40 mHz) generator, which is actually a modified radio transmitter. This radio frequency (RF) source is located near the materials to be joined. This high-frequency source causes the molecules in the plastic to attempt an alignment. The RF source changes the poles of the current at the rate of the process frequency. These rapidly changing poles cause sufficient molecular motion within the plastic to generate frictional heat and soften the plastic, allowing it to be joined with additional pressure. See Fig. 10-21.

Joining of Plastics

Mechanical Fasteners

Mechanical fasteners are the conventional fastening systems that have been used to join nonplastic parts for hundreds of years. They include: screws, snaps, nuts and bolts, and clips.

The only significant technical development in mechanical fasteners for plastic parts is the self-tapping screw. The self-tapping screw holds plastic assemblies together by creating a female thread in the plastic parts as the screw is installed.

Self-tapping screws are excellent for joining plastic parts that will never be disassembled, but the quality of the thread is inadequate for multiple assembly or disassembly.

Overall, these mechanical fasteners should be avoided when designing plastic parts. Fasteners introduce added cost, reduced quality, and a higher inventory cost for the product manufacturer.

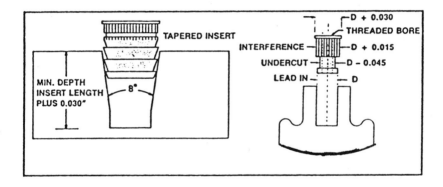

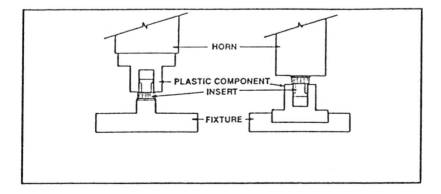

Fig. 10-22 Ultrasonic insertion. Source: Branson Ultrasonics Corporation, Danbury, CT

Heat Staking

Heat staking is the process of using a heated tool to melt a plastic boss and join two parts together. The heat staking tool is similar to the ultrasonic staking tool illustrated in Fig. 10-20. Heat staking is often seen as a possible alternative to ultrasonic staking mainly because the heat staking equipment is much simpler and much lower in cost.

The disadvantage associated with heat staking is that the plastic being heated may not be heated uniformly, and as a result the mechanical strength of the stake may be reduced.

Heat staking is especially useful in areas where ultrasonic staking is impossible, such as staking flexible materials that are low energy transmitters.

Ultrasonic Staking and Inserting

As mentioned earlier in this chapter, ultrasonics can be used to stake and insert metal into plastic. All of the energy transmittance conditions apply to staking and inserting with ultrasonics. The horn geometry must conform to the requirements of the assembly process and still be in tune. See Fig. 10-22. This may require having the ultrasonic equipment manufacturer produce the horn to meet specific applications.

Fig. 10-23 Metal inserts for plastics, available in a wide variety of shapes and sizes. Source: Heli-Coil Division, Emhart Corporation

Staking. The staking of a boss with ultrasonics is similar to heat staking. The design of the boss to be staked can be identical to a heat stake boss. The advantage of ultrasonic staking is control. The shape of the stake and the melt process can be better controlled.

Inserting. The use of metal ultrasonic inserts is beneficial for several reasons, including:

- Reducing the complexity of the secondary operations
- Providing a uniform thread size
- Providing a wear resistant, metal thread area for multiple assembly and disassembly

The inserts are specifically designed to be used with the ultrasonic process and are often made with brass or aluminum. See Fig. 10-23 and 10-24. The exterior of the insert is knurled to provide good holding power and torque resistance. The interior of the insert is machined with a class 2 female thread to meet the requirements of the application.

Inserts can be located manually or automatically onto the plastic part. In most cases the plastic part will have a hole or hollow boss with a hole diameter

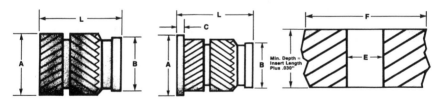

INSERT SPECIFICATIONS					HOLE SIZE RECOMMENDATIONS	
Standard Ultrasert IV		Diameter		Length	Hole Size	Minimum Boss Diameter
Thread Size	Part Number	A ±.004	B ±.003	L ±.004	E +.003 −.000	F
2-56	UB000256	.143	.123	.157	.126	.286
4-40	UB000440	.186	.154	.226	.156	.372
6-32	UB000632	.217	.185	.281	.188	.434
8-32	UB000832	.249	.218	.321	.221	.498
10-24	UB001024	.279	.249	.375	.252	.558
10-32	UB001032	.279	.249	.375	.252	.558
1/4-20	UB001420	.340	.312	.500	.315	.680
1/4-28	UB001428	.340	.312	.500	.315	.680
5/16-18	UB051618	.406	.374	.500	.377	.812
5/16-24	UB051624	.406	.374	.500	.377	.812
3/8-16	UB003816	.463	.434	.500	.439	.926
3/8-24	UB003824	.463	.434	.500	.439	.926

Fig. 10-24 Ultrasonic insert sizing. Source: Heli-Coil Division, Emhart Corporation

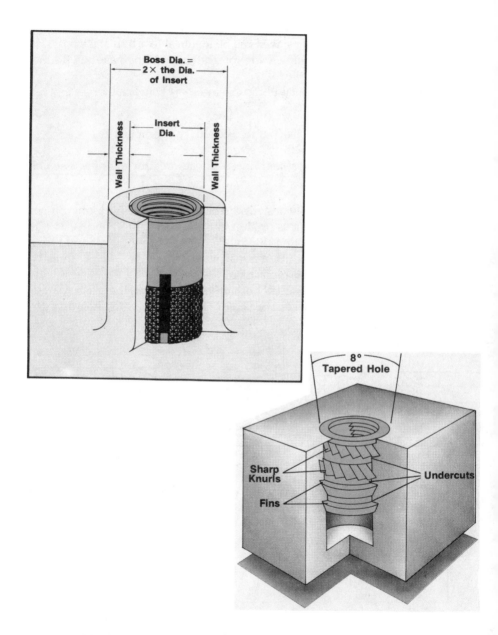

Fig. 10-25 Metal inserts in plastic parts. Source: Heli-Coil Division, Emhart Corporation

sized to locate the insert only. See Fig. 10-25. The hole size must be carefully specified to provide interference with the insert and plastic material that is sufficient to hold the insert securely in place.

The strength and quality of the inserting process can be measured with a "pull-out" test and/or a torque test. See Table 10-1 and Fig. 10-26. The quality of the insertion process is a function of the insert design, the part design, and the ultrasonic parameters.

Table 10-1 Insert Troubleshooting Guide

Problem	Solution	Problem	Solution
Insufficient pull-out or torque strength	Decrease pressure Increase weld time Increase amplitude (change booster)	**Damage to insert**	Decrease weld time Decrease amplitude (change booster) Increase pressure
Plastic cracks	Make sure ultrasonics are on Decrease pressure Increase wall thickness	**Partial Insertion**	Increase pressure Decrease down speed Decrease amplitude (change booster)
Inserting time is excessive	Decrease weld time Decrease hold time Decrease amplitude (change booster)	**System overloads**	Decrease pressure Decrease down speed Decrease amplitude, (change booster)

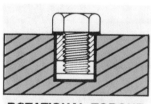

ROTATIONAL TORQUE
Rotational force required to turn the insert in the parent material. It is a good comparative measure of overall strength of the assembly.

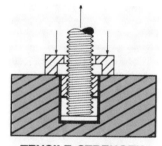

TENSILE STRENGTH
Axial force (in pounds) required to pull the insert out of the material at least .020.

Fig. 10-26 Testing metal insert strength after installation in a plastic part. Source: Heli-Coil Division, Emhart Corporation

One key advantage of ultrasonic inserting over other inserting processes, especially the cold insertion of inserts into plastic, is that the ultrasonic process provides a low stress level and a high repeatability.

Degating. One of the most unique applications for ultrasonics in the plastics industry is the degating of plastic parts. All the principles and equipment associated with ultrasonic welding of plastics applies to the degating of plastic parts.

Thermoplastic parts are usually designed to reduce or eliminate the need for degating. Degating is time consuming, labor intensive, and can easily have a negative effect on product quality.

Over the past 10 years, designing for manufacturing concepts have led to the resurgence of family molds that require the variety of parts molded, each cycle, to remain on the runner system to ensure a complete part set or kit.

Ultrasonics have been employed to facilitate the degating of these parts without the use of sharp cutting tools and in a manner that can be automated.

The principle is simple. See Fig. 10-27. The molded parts on the runner "tree" are placed in a nest designed specifically to hold the runner and not the part. The ultrasonic horn is allowed to contact the runner system in such a way as to maximize the energy transmittance throughout the runner.

The gate becomes a quasi-energy director that focuses the high-frequency mechanical vibrations. This activity will soften the plastic in the gate and separate the part from the gate cleanly.

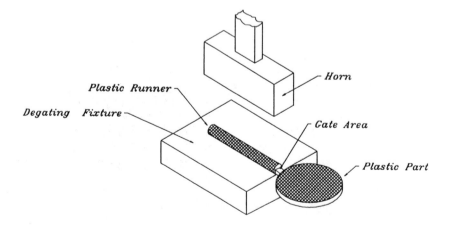

Fig. 10-27 Degating plastic parts without cutting

Snap Fits

Snap fits are design features that can be incorporated in many plastic part design systems. Snap fits eliminate mechanical fasteners and adhesives, thus allowing for a lower cost assembly.

The effectiveness of a snap fit is directly related to material properties (flexural modulus and flexibility) and product design (displacement of snap).

Other factors include the frequency or number of snaps required, *i.e.*, whether there will be only one snap in the life of the product or multiple snaps.

The snap fit has been used successfully in a wide variety of designs (see Fig. 10-28):

- External snap (round) used in closures
- Internal snap (round) used in closures
- Ball and socket
- Cantilever snap

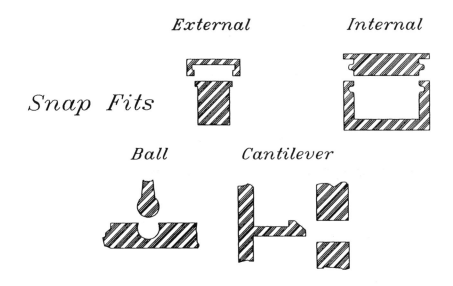

Fig. 10-28 Various plastic snap-fit designs

The cantilever snap can be accomplished by using three basic designs (see Fig. 10-29):

- Edge—requires no special mold actions
- Surface—requires expensive mold side core action
- Surface with hole—a low-cost alternative to surface that does not require expensive side core action

Within these snap-fit designs there are several variations, including the use of multiple snaps. The cantilever snap fit can best be understood by considering the mechanics of the snap design. A straight cantilever snap fit is shown in Fig. 10-30.

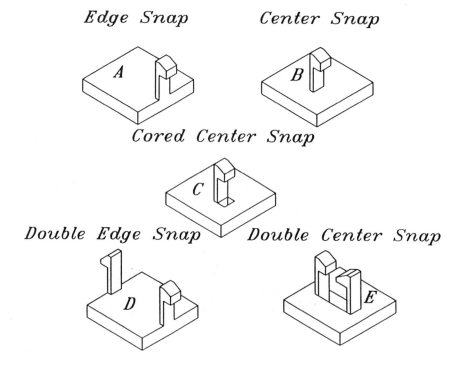

Fig. 10-29 Snap-fit designs using cantilevered arms

The moment of inertia, I, is a function of the geometry of the beam. Most material manufacturers will provide the designer with all the key design criteria.

Note from the equation that if the flexural modulus (E) of the plastic material increases (the plastic gets stiffer), the force to snap increases. Also note that as the length of the beam gets longer, the force to deflect decreases.

The part designer should always consult the plastic material supplier to be sure the snap design and requirements do not exceed the capability of the plastic material.

Designing for Manufacturing

The concepts highlighted in most discussions about designing for manufacturing and assembly are basically documented conventional wisdom. The ideas are not new, but they are often forgotten elements of common sense that require very little expense to incorporate in the early stage of the product design.

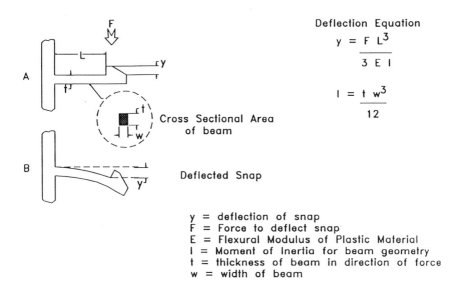

Deflection Equation

$$y = \frac{F\,L^3}{3\,E\,I}$$

$$I = \frac{t\,w^3}{12}$$

Cross Sectional Area of beam

Deflected Snap

y = deflection of snap
F = Force to deflect snap
E = Flexural Modulus of Plastic Material
I = Moment of Inertia for beam geometry
t = thickness of beam in direction of force
w = width of beam

Fig. 10-30 Straight cantilever snap fit

For years, many manufacturers had the product design personnel separated from the everyday struggles of product manufacturing. Today many world-class manufacturers are pooling their technical resources early in the design cycle to develop realistic and highly manufacturable products.

There are several key tenets to designing a product for manufacturing. A few of these concepts include:

- Reducing parts, including the elimination of mechanical fasteners. See Fig. 10-31
- Maximizing the functionality of parts; having parts perform more than one function
- Reducing secondary decorating; having color contained within the plastic
- Facilitating assembly by incorporating tapers and chamfers. See Fig. 10-32
- Reducing assembly errors by nesting and orienting parts to be joined. See Fig. 10-33

By understanding the product assembly requirements, the designer can add product features that will save time and improve product quality.

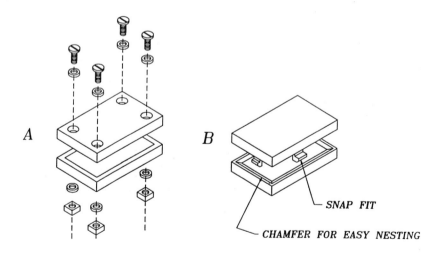

Fig. 10-31 Designing a product without mechanical fasteners

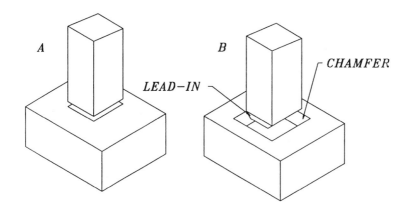

Fig. 10-32 Designing a product with tapers and chamfers

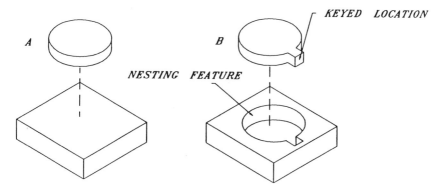

Fig. 10-33 Designing a product with nesting parts

Most of the discussion regarding design for manufacturing is associated with injection-molded parts; however, extruded profiles offer a unique design challenge.

Consider a flexible profile that is bonded to a rigid profile. See Fig. 10-34. By including a slight design change to both parts, replacement of the flexible profile can be made easier, and product life will be extended.

For the designer of products made using plastics that are not bondable, or where adhesives are undesirable, a channel or slot design feature may provide the same result at a lower cost. See Fig. 10-35.

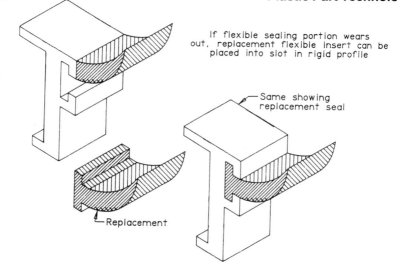

If flexible sealing portion wears
out, replacement flexible insert can be
placed into slot in rigid profile

Same showing
replacement seal

Replacement

Fig. 10-34 Bondable materials

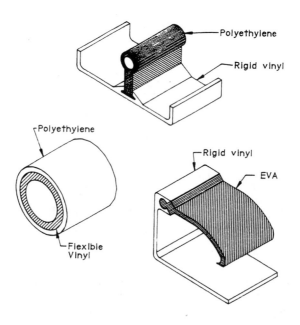

Polyethylene

Rigid vinyl

Polyethylene

Rigid vinyl

EVA

Flexible
Vinyl

Fig. 10-35 Nonbondable materials joined by mechanical keying or fit

Plastics lend themselves to design for manufacturing techniques and will continue to be a cost improvement medium for product designers.

Designing for Disassembly

Significant resources and engineering efforts are being expended on designing plastic parts, and other materials, for assembly and manufacturing. Note that there is also a need to develop and use criteria for designing for disassembly.

Large users of plastic, such as the automotive industry, are considering how to dispose of their products after the useful life of the product is over.

As mentioned in earlier chapters, one of the main environmental concerns associated with using plastic is the need to have a viable material identification system to allow postconsumer reclaimers an opportunity to harvest the plastic for reuse. In addition, the products that contain plastic need to be easily disassembled to facilitate the reclaiming process.

The challenge for future designers is to provide low-cost, easy-to-assemble products that meet all the customer's requirements and are designed for easy disassembly to facilitate material recycling.

Appendix A: Tradename Directory*

A

A & B EPOXY PASTE (two-part epoxy adhesive (reg. & fast)) Hexcel Corporation, Resins Group

ABBEY 100 (conductive PVC compounds) Abbey Plastics Corporation

ABSACON (glass concentrated ABS) Akzo/Wilson Fiberfil

ABSAFIL (reinforced ABS) Akzo/Wilson Fiberfil

ACCUPUNCH (in line automated punch for punching, cutting, blanking plastic & rubber profiles) Extrusion Services, Inc.

ACCUTHANE (one comp. urethane adhesive) H.B. Fuller Company

ACLAR (CTFE fluorohalocarbon films) Allied Signal Inc. Engineered Plastics

ACOUSTO-ULTRASONIC (nondestructive testing unit for flaw detection and strength evaluation in fiberglass laminates and p) HSB Inspection Technologies

ACRA-COLOR (material blender) Thoreson-Mccosh, Inc.

ACRYLAFIL (reinforced SAN) Akzo/Wilson Fiberfil

ACRYLITE (acrylic sheet, and molding and extrusion compounds) Cyro Industries

AIRWELD (super-heated air sealing system) Amscomatic, Inc.

ALATHON (polyethylene resins) Cain Chemical

ALPHA (PVC compounds) Dexter Plastics, Alpha Compounds

ALPHA VYNITE (PVC/nitrile rubber alloys) Dexter Plastics, Alpha Compounds

AMBASSADOR (billiard ball, phenolic) Hyatt Ball Company Ltd. Marblette

ANTI-STICK (food grade mold release) Price-Driscoll Corporation

ANTISTAT (Antistatic Agents 17200) Morflex Chemical Company, Inc. Special Chemicals Dept.

ARBURG (injection molding machines) Polymer Machinery Corporation

ARDEL (polyarylate) Amoco Performance Products

ARLOY (engineering resins) Arco Chemical Co.

ARMID (aliphatic amides) Akzo Chemicals Inc. Chemical Division

ARMOSTAT (antistatic agents) Akzo Chemicals Inc. Chemical Division

*Condensed from *Plastics World, 1989*, Cahners Publishing Co., 275 Washington St., Newton, MA.

ARPRO (expanded polypropylene beads) Arco Chemical Company
ARYLON (polyarylate resins) Du Pont, E.I., De Nemours & Company, Inc.
Polymer Products, Engineering Resins
ASTRO SET (formaldehyde resins) Astro Industries, Inc.

B

BAKELITE (PE resins and compounds) Union Carbide Polyolefins Division
BANBURY (internal batch mixer) Farrel Corporation
BAREX (nitrile barrier resin) Standard Oil Chemical Company
BAYBLEND (ABS/polycarbonate blends) Mobay Corporation Plastics and
Rubber Division
BAYDUR (rigid structural urethane foam) Mobay Corporation Polyurethane
Division
BAYFLEX (elastomeric urethane foam chemicals) Mobay Corporation
Polyurethane Division
BEETLE (urea-formaldehyde) American Cyanamid Company, Polymer
Products Division, Venture Chemicals Division
BUNA (elastomers, ethylene propylene, polybutadiene styrene) Huls
America Inc.
BUTVAR (polyvinyl butyral) Monsanto Company

C

CAB-O-SIL (fumed silica) Cabot Corporation Cab-O-Sil Division
CADON (styrene maleic anhydride terpolymers) Monsanto Company
CAPRAN (nylon films and sheet) Allied Signal Inc. Engineered Plastics
CAPRON (nylon resins and compounds) Allied Signal Inc. Engineered Plastics
tics
CELANEX (thermoplastic polyester) Celanese Engineering Resins Division of
Celanese Corporation
CELCON (acetal copolymer) Celanese Engineering Resins Division of
Celanese Corporation
CELLOSIZE (hydroxyethyl cellulose thickening agent) Union Carbide Cor-
poration Solvents & Coatings Materials Division
CELOGEN (chemical blowing agents for plastics) Santech Inc.
CHEM-O-SOL (PVC plastisols) Whittaker Corporation Providence Chemi-
cals Division
CHROMALOX (industrial process electric heating equipment and tempera-
ture controls) Chromalox E.L. Wiegand Division
CONATHANE (polyurethane resins and elastomers) Conap, Inc.
CRYSTALENE (low density polyethylene sheeting) Crystal-X-Corporation

CYCOLAC (ABS/resin) General Electric Company Plastics Group
CYCOLOY (ABS/polycarbonate alloy) General Electric Company Plastics Group
CYCOVIN (ABS/PVC alloy) General Electric Company Plastics Group

D

DACRON (synthetic fibers) Du Pont, E.I., De Nemours & Company, Inc. Textile Fibers Dept.
DAY-GLO (daylight fluorescent colorants) Day-Glo Color Corporation
D.E.R. (epoxy resins) Dow Chemical U.S.A.
DERAKANE (vinyl ester resins) Dow Chemical U.S.A.
DESMOBOND (polyurethane structural adhesive) Mobay Corporation Inorganic Chemicals Division
DIENE (polybutadiene) Firestone Synthetic Rubber & Latex Company Division of Firestone Tire & Rubber Company
DODGE (fastening inserts) Heli-Coil Division Emhart Corporation
DRI-AIR (dehumidifiers and hopper dryers) Boy Machines, Inc.
DYLARK (engineering resins) Arco Chemical Company
DYLENE (polystyrene) Arco Chemical Company
DYNA-PURGE (purging compound) Shuman Plastics Inc.

E

EASTOBOND (adhesives) Eastman Chemical Products, Inc. Sub. of Eastman Kodak Company, Plastics Division
EASYPOXY (epoxy adhesives) Conap, Inc.
ELASTALLOY (thermoplastic elastomer) GLS Plastic Division Great Lakes Terminal & Transport
ELECTRONIC PLASTI-CORDER (electronic torque rheometer) C.W. Brabender Instruments Inc.
ELVALOY (plasticizers, impact modifiers) Du Pont, E.I., De Nemours & Company, Inc. Polymer Products, Polymer Additives
EPON (epoxy resin) Shell Canada Chemical Company
ESTANE (thermoplastic polyurethane) Goodrich, B F, Geon Vinyl Division
ETHAFOAM (plastic foam (PE & cross-linked PE)) Dow Chemical U.S.A.

F

FADE-OMETER (light stability tester, light fastness tester) Custom Scientific Instruments, Inc.
FASTWELD 10 (adhesive system) Ciba-Geigy/ESG/REN

FINA (polystyrene) Fina Oil & Chemical Company
FINA (polypropylene) Fina Oil & Chemical Company
FLUON (polytetrafluoroethylene, industrial grades) ICI Americas, Inc.
FORTAFIL (carbon fibers) Fortafil Fibers
FREKOTE RELEASING INTERFACE (mold release agent) Hysol Division, The Dexter Corporation Frekote Products
FREON (physical blowing agents) Du Pont, E.I., De Nemours & Company Inc. Chemicals & Pigments Dept.
FUSON (heat transfer decals for decoration) The Meyercord Company Printed Products Group

G

GARDNER (viscometers) Pacific Scientific Instrument Division
GELOY (weatherable resin) General Electric Company Plastics Group
GEON (vinyls) Goodrich, B F, Geon Vinyl Division
GLASKYD (alkyd molding compounds) American Cyanamid Company Polymer Products Division, Venture Chemicals Division
GLASTIC (fiberglass reinforced plastics) Glastic Company Division of Nortek, Inc.

H

HELI-COIL (fastening inserts) Heli-Coil Division Emhart Corporation
HUNZIKER (automatic deflashing machines) W. Hunziker Company Distributed by S&B Marketing Inc.
HYSOL (all company products) Hysol Division The Dexter Corporation

I

ISOCHEM (hardner) Furane Products/Isochem Operations Subs. of Rohm and Haas Advanced Materials Company

J

JIFFY-TITE (heaters/coolers) D-M-E Company A Fairchild Industries Company

K

KEL-F (CTFE) 3-M Company Industrial Chem Prod. Division
KODAR (polyester, copolymer, thermoplastic) Eastman Chemical Pro-ducts, Inc. Sub. of Eastman Kodak Company, Plastics Division
KONA BUSHING (heat pipe hot sprue bushing) Kona Corporation

KRATON (thermoplastic rubber) Shell Chemical Company Division of Shell Oil Company
K-RESIN (butadiene styrene polymers) Phillips 66 Company A Subsid. of Phillips Petroleum Company
KYNAR (polyvinylidene fluoride and copolymer) Pennwalt Corporation Plastics Dept.

L

LEXAN (polycarbonate resins, sheet) General Electric Company Plastics Group
LOGIC SEAL (negative pressure pump) Logic Devices, Inc.
LOMOD (engineering elastomers) General Electric Company, Plastics Group
LUPERSOL (catalysts, organic peroxide) Lucidol Division Pennwalt
LUSTRAN ABS (acrylonitrile-butadiene-styrene) Monsanto Company
LUSTRAN SAN (styrene-acrylonitrile) Monsanto Company

M

MAGNUM (ABS resin) Dow Chemical U.S.A.
MAKROBLEND (polycarbonate/polyester) Mobay Corporation Inorganic Chemicals Division
MAKROLON (polycarbonate) Mobay Corporation Inorganic Chemicals Division
MARLEX (polyethylene, high and low density, polypropylene resins) Phillips 66 Company A Subsid. of Phillips Petroleum Company
MAXI-BLAST (cylindrical polycarbonate deflashing media) Maxi-Blast, Inc.
MERLON (polycarbonate) Mobay Corporation Plastics And Rubber Division
MICA C (muscovite mica) Spartan Minerals Corporation
MICARTA (thermoset paper, linen or canvas-phenolic sheet glass-melamine or epoxy sheet) Liberty POLYGLAS, Inc.
MICROBEADS (glass beads) Ferro Corporation Cataphote Division
MINLON (engineering thermoplastic resins) Du Pont, E.I., De Nemours & Company, Inc. Polymer Products, Engineering Resins
MOLD SWEEP (parts handling device) Martin Industries
MORGAN-PRESS (injection molding machine, thermoplastic) Morgan Industries

N

NEOPRENE   (chloroprene) Du Pont, E.I., De Nemours & Company, Inc. Polymer Products Dept., Elastomers

NORYL   (phenylene oxide-based resins) General Electric Company Noryl Products Division

NOVALOY   (plastic alloys for injection molding, extrusion, and sheet) Novatec Plastics & Chemicals Company, Inc.

NYLATRON (nylon stock shapes, fabricated parts & molding resins) Polymer Corporation

P

PARAPLEX (adipate based polyesters) The C.P. Hall Company

PARAPLEX (polymeric plasticizers) Hall, C.P. Company

PAXON (HDPE resins) Allied Corporation HPDE

PETLON (polyester, thermoplastic (PET-type)) Mobay Corporation Inorganic Chemicals Division

PETRA (PET resins) Allied Signal Inc. Engineered Plastics

PETROTHENE (polyethylene and polypropylene resins) Quantum Chemical Corporation USI Division

PLASKON (epoxy molding compounds) Plaskon Electronic Materials

PLASTI-CORDER (torque rheometer) C.W. Brabender Instruments Inc.

PLENCO (thermoset molding compounds) Plastic Engineering Company

PLEXIGLAS (acrylic sheet and molding resins) Rohm and Haas Company Plastics Division

PLIOBOND (elastomer adhesive) Bond Adhesives Company

PLIOLITE   (styrene-butadiene resins) Goodyear Tire & Rubber Company Chemical Division

POLIFIL (reinforced thermoplastics calcium carbonate-reinforced poly a. calcium carbonate; b. talc; c. mica) Polifil, Inc.

POLYMER C (low viscosity amorphous PP for use as microcrystalline wax replacement or extender) Crowley Chemical Company, Inc.

POLYAMPROLENE   (pelletized amorphous PE/PP to provide non-slip properties to film) Crowley Chemical Company, Inc.

POLYCARBAFIL (reinforced polycarbonate) Akzo/Wilson Fiberfil

POLYDAP (fiberglass reinforced diallyl phthallate & diallyl isophalate) Industrial Dielectrics, Inc.

POLYFLAM (flame retardant thermoplastics (P/E, P/P, P/S and ABS)) Schulman, A., Inc.

POLYLITE (polyester resins) Reichold Chemicals, Inc.

POLYSAR (polystyrene resins) Polysar Inc. Plastics Division

POLYVIN (flexible and semi-rigid PVC) Schulman, A., Inc.

PROCON (glass concentrated polypropylene) Akzo/Wilson Fiberfil

PRO-FAX (polypropylene) Himont U.S.A., Inc.

PROFIL (reinforced polypropylene) Akzo/Wilson Fiberfil

PULSE (engineering resins (PC/ABS)) Dow Chemical U.S.A.

R

RABIT (horizontal injection molding machines pneumatic toggle clamp to 2.5 grams hydraulic toggle clamp to 4.5 grams) Mar-Tech, Incorporated

RESINOL (polyolefin sheet—L.D.P.E., H.D.P.E. P.P.) Norton Company Performance Plastics Division

RILSAN (nylon 11 & 12 resins) Atochem Canada Inc.

ROYALITE (ABS, PVC and ABS/PVC sheet, PVC/acrylic sheet) Uniroyal Plastic Products

RX (phenolic) Rogers Corporation

RYNITE (thermoplastic polyester resins) Du Pont, E.I., De Nemours & Company, Inc. Polymer Products, Engineering Resins

RYTON (polyphenylene sulfide resins and compounds) Phillips 66 Company A Subsid. of Phillips Petroleum Company

S

SANTOPRENE (polypropylene/EPDM-thermoplastic rubber) Monsanto Company

SARAN (PVDC resins, HB mono layer high barrier film) Dow Chemical U.S.A.

SILAPRENE (industrial adhesives & sealants for OEM) UniRoyal Plastics Company Adhesives Division

SILASTIC (silicone rubber) Dow Corning Corporation

SILVERCONE (hot stamping die) Gladen Corporation

SIMCO (electrostatic locators, film cleaners and static neutralizing bars) Simco Company, Inc.

SMA RESINS (styrene maleic anhydride resins) Sartomer Company

STATI MIXER (line of motionless mixers) Chemineer Kenics

STATICIDE (antistatic topical coating and acrylic conductive floor finish, cleaner and acrylic floor stripper) ACL Incorporated

STELLITE (cobalt base powder alloys) Stellite Coatings Division Stoody-Deloru-Stellite

STYRAFIL (reinforced polystyrene) Akzo/Wilson Fiberfil
SUPER-X (LLDPE film) Poly Pak America, Inc.
SURLYN (ionomer resins) Du Pont, E.I., De Nemours & Company, Inc.
Polymer Products, Ethylene Polymers

T

TEFLON (fluorocarbon resins) Du Pont, E.I., De Nemours & Company, Inc.
Polymer Products, Fluoropolymers
TEFZEL (fluoropolymer) Du Pont, E.I., De Nemours & Company, Inc.
Polymer Products, Fluoropolymers
TENITE (resins) Eastman Chemical Products, Inc. Sub. of Eastman Kodak
Company, Plastics Division
TETRALENE (ultra-high molecular weight polyethylene compounds)
Tetrafluor, Inc.
TEXIN (polyurethane, thermoplastic) Mobay Corporation Rubber Divi-sion
THERIMAGE (heat-transfer decorating method) Dennison Mfg. Company
THERMAL PIN (heat conductors designed for plastic molds to reduce cycle
time and improve part quality) Noren Products, Inc.
TITANOX (titanium dioxide and color concentrates) NL Chemicals, Inc.
TROGAMID T (transparent nylon) Dynamit Nobel Chemicals
TRYCITE (polystyrene film) Dow Chemical U.S.A.
TYGON (flexible plastic tubing) Norton Company Performance Plastics
TYRIL (styrene-acrylonitrile) Dow Chemical U.S.A.

U

UDEL (polysulfone) Amoco Performance Products
ULTEM (polyetherimide resins) General Electric Company Plastics Group
ULTRA AR (crosslinked outdoor stabilized UHMW) UltraPoly Inc.
ULTRABLEND (engineering thermoplastics blends/alloys) BASF Corpora-
tion Engineering Plastics
ULTRAMID (nylon resins) BASF Corporation Engineering Plastics
URAFIL (reinforced polyurethane) Akzo/Wilson Fiberfil
URALAC (thermoset polyesters) DSM Resins US, Inc.

V

VYDYNE (nylon 6/6 resins) Monsanto Company

W

WELLAMID (nylons, tapes 6 and 6/6) Wellman Inc. Plastic Division

X

XALOY (screws & barrels, bi-metallic) Plastic Equip. of Kansas City
XENOY (polycarbonate-based alloy blends) General Electric Company Plastics Group
XT POLYMER (acrylic-based multipolymer compounds) Cyro Industries
XYDAR (liquid crystal polymer) Amoco Performance Products

Z

ZYTEL (nylon resins) Du Pont, E.I., De Nemours & Company, Inc. Polymer Products, Engineering Resins

Appendix B: Sample Tolerance Guidelines

Standards & Practices of Plastics Molders	Material
	Acrylic

Note: The *Commercial* values shown below represent common production tolerances at the most economical level. The *Fine* values represent closer tolerances that can be held but at a greater cost. Any addition of fillers will compromise physical properties and alter dimensional stability. Please consult the manufacturer.

Drawing Code	Dimensions (Inches)		
A = Diameter (See note #1)	0.000 / 0.500 / 1.000 / 2.000		
B = Depth (See note #3)	3.000		
C = Height (See note #3)	4.000 / 5.000 / 6.000		

Plus or Minus in Thousands of an Inch (5, 10, 15, 20, 25) — *Commercial* and *Fine* curves shown.

		Comm. ±	Fine ±
	6.000 to 12.000 for each additional inch add (inches)	0.004	0.002
D = Bottom Wall	(See note #9)	0.005	0.002
E = Side Wall	(See note #2)	0.004	0.002
F = Hole Size Diameter (See note #1)	0.000 to 0.125	0.003	0.001
	0.126 to 0.250	0.003	0.002
	0.251 to 0.500	0.004	0.002
	0.501 & over	0.005	0.003
G = Hole Size Depth (See note #5)	0.000 to 0.250	0.004	0.002
	0.251 to 0.500	0.004	0.002
	0.501–1.000	0.006	0.003
H = Corners, Ribs, Fillets	(See note #6)	0.025	0.012
Flatness	0.000 to 3.000	0.013	0.008
(See note #4)	3.001 to 6.000	0.023	0.015
Thread Size (Class)	Internal	1	2
	External	1	2
Concentricity	(See note #4) (F.I.M.)	0.010	0.006
Draft Allowance per side	(See note #5)	1.5°	0.75°
Surface finish	(See note #8)		
Color Stability	(See note #7)		

REFERENCE NOTES

1. These tolerances do not include allowance for aging characteristics of material

2. Wall thickness should be as uniform as possible.

3. Parting line must be taken into consideration.

4. Part design should maintain a wall thickness as nearly constant as possible. Complete uniformity in this dimension is sometimes impossible to achieve. Walls of non-uniform thickness should be gradually blended from thick to thin.

5. Care must be taken that the ratio of the depth of a cored hole to its diameter does not reach a point that will result in excessive pin damage.

6. Large radius is desirable to minimize part breakage.

7. Customer-Molder understanding is necessary prior to tooling.

8. Part surface finish is dependent on mold finish.

9. Based on nominal 0.125 inch wall.

Reprinted from *Standards & Practices of Plastic Molders*, courtesy of The Society of the Plastics, Industry, Inc.

| Standards & Practices of Plastics Molders | | Material: Melamine - Phenolic (MF-PF) |

Note: The *Commercial* values shown below represent common production tolerances at the most economical level. The *Fine* values represent closer tolerances that can be held but at a greater cost. Any addition of fillers will compromise physical properties and alter dimensional stability. Please consult the manufacturer.

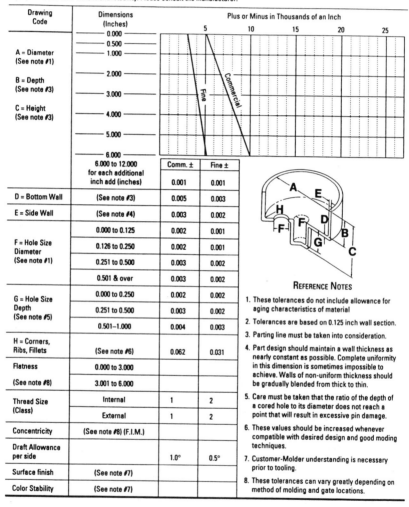

Drawing Code	Dimensions (Inches)	Comm. ±	Fine ±
A = Diameter (See note #1) B = Depth (See note #3) C = Height (See note #3)	0.000, 0.500, 1.000, 2.000, 3.000, 4.000, 5.000, 6.000 (graph)		
	6.000 to 12.000 for each additional inch add (inches)	0.001	0.001
D = Bottom Wall	(See note #3)	0.005	0.003
E = Side Wall	(See note #4)	0.003	0.002
F = Hole Size Diameter (See note #1)	0.000 to 0.125	0.002	0.001
	0.126 to 0.250	0.002	0.001
	0.251 to 0.500	0.003	0.002
	0.501 & over	0.003	0.002
G = Hole Size Depth (See note #5)	0.000 to 0.250	0.002	0.002
	0.251 to 0.500	0.003	0.002
	0.501–1.000	0.004	0.003
H = Corners, Ribs, Fillets	(See note #6)	0.062	0.031
Flatness (See note #8)	0.000 to 3.000		
	3.001 to 6.000		
Thread Size (Class)	Internal	1	2
	External	1	2
Concentricity	(See note #8) (F.I.M.)		
Draft Allowance per side		1.0°	0.5°
Surface finish	(See note #7)		
Color Stability	(See note #7)		

REFERENCE NOTES

1. These tolerances do not include allowance for aging characteristics of material
2. Tolerances are based on 0.125 inch wall section.
3. Parting line must be taken into consideration.
4. Part design should maintain a wall thickness as nearly constant as possible. Complete uniformity in this dimension is sometimes impossible to achieve. Walls of non-uniform thickness should be gradually blended from thick to thin.
5. Care must be taken that the ratio of the depth of a cored hole to its diameter does not reach a point that will result in excessive pin damage.
6. These values should be increased whenever compatible with desired design and good moding techniques.
7. Customer-Molder understanding is necessary prior to tooling.
8. These tolerances can vary greatly depending on method of molding and gate locations.

Reprinted from *Standards & Practices of Plastic Molders*, courtesy of The Society of the Plastics Industry, Inc.

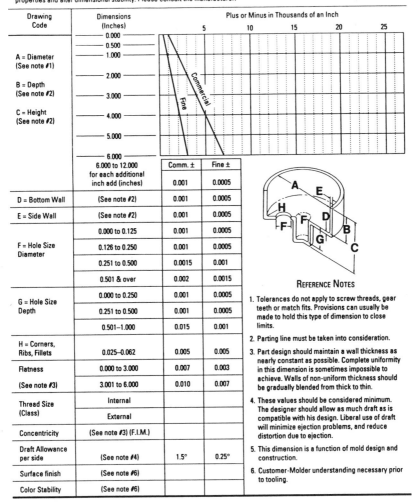

Standards & Practices of Plastics Molders		Material Polyetherimide (PEI)

Note: The *Commercial* values shown below represent common production tolerances at the most economical level. The *Fine* values represent closer tolerances that can be held but at a greater cost. Any addition of fillers will compromise physical properties and alter dimensional stability. Please consult the manufacturer.

Drawing Code	Dimensions (Inches)	Comm. ±	Fine ±
A = Diameter (See note #1)	6.000 to 12.000 for each additional inch add (inches)	0.001	0.0005
B = Depth (See note #2)			
C = Height (See note #2)			
D = Bottom Wall	(See note #2)	0.001	0.0005
E = Side Wall	(See note #2)	0.001	0.0005
F = Hole Size Diameter	0.000 to 0.125	0.001	0.0005
	0.126 to 0.250	0.001	0.0005
	0.251 to 0.500	0.0015	0.001
	0.501 & over	0.002	0.0015
G = Hole Size Depth	0.000 to 0.250	0.001	0.0005
	0.251 to 0.500	0.001	0.0005
	0.501–1.000	0.015	0.001
H = Corners, Ribs, Fillets	0.025–0.062	0.005	0.005
Flatness	0.000 to 3.000	0.007	0.003
(See note #3)	3.001 to 6.000	0.010	0.007
Thread Size (Class)	Internal		
	External		
Concentricity	(See note #3) (F.I.M.)		
Draft Allowance per side	(See note #4)	1.5°	0.25°
Surface finish	(See note #6)		
Color Stability	(See note #6)		

Plus or Minus in Thousands of an Inch

REFERENCE NOTES

1. Tolerances do not apply to screw threads, gear teeth or match fits. Provisions can usually be made to hold this type of dimension to close limits.

2. Parting line must be taken into consideration.

3. Part design should maintain a wall thickness as nearly constant as possible. Complete uniformity in this dimension is sometimes impossible to achieve. Walls of non-uniform thickness should be gradually blended from thick to thin.

4. These values should be considered minimum. The designer should allow as much draft as is compatible with his design. Liberal use of draft will minimize ejection problems, and reduce distortion due to ejection.

5. This dimension is a function of mold design and construction.

6. Customer-Molder understanding necessary prior to tooling.

Reprinted from *Standards & Practices of Plastic Molders*, courtesy of The Society of the Plastics Industry, Inc.

Standards & Practices of Plastics Molders		Material Phenol-Formaldehyde (PF) (Phenolic) Glass Filled

Note: The *Commercial* values shown below represent common production tolerances at the most economical level. The *Fine* values represent closer tolerances that can be held but at a greater cost. Any addition of fillers will compromise physical properties and alter dimensional stability. Please consult the manufacturer.

Drawing Code	Dimensions (Inches)	Plus or Minus in Thousands of an Inch				
		5	10	15	20	25

Drawing Code	Dimensions (Inches)	Comm. ±	Fine ±
A = Diameter (See note #1) B = Depth (See note #3) C = Height (See note #3)	0.000 / 0.500 / 1.000 / 2.000 / 3.000 / 4.000 / 5.000 / 6.000		
	6.000 to 12.000 for each additional inch add (inches)	0.001	0.001
D = Bottom Wall	(See note #3)	0.005	0.003
E = Side Wall	(See note #4)	0.001	0.001
F = Hole Size Diameter (See note #1)	0.000 to 0.125	0.001	0.001
	0.126 to 0.250	0.001	0.001
	0.251 to 0.500	0.001	0.001
	0.501 & over	0.002	0.001
G = Hole Size Depth (See note #5)	0.000 to 0.250	0.001	0.001
	0.251 to 0.500	0.001	0.001
	0.501–1.000	0.002	0.001
H = Corners, Ribs, Fillets	(See note #6)	0.062	0.031
Flatness	0.000 to 3.000		
(See note #8)	3.001 to 6.000		
Thread Size (Class)	Internal	1	2
	External	1	2
Concentricity	(See note #8) (F.I.M.)	0.005	0.003
Draft Allowance per side		1.0°	0.5°
Surface finish	(See note #7)		
Color Stability	(See note #7)		

REFERENCE NOTES

1. These tolerances do not include allowance for aging characteristics of material
2. Tolerances are based on 0.125 inch wall section.
3. Parting line must be taken into consideration.
4. Part design should maintain a wall thickness as nearly constant as possible. Complete uniformity in this dimension is sometimes impossible to achieve. Walls of non-uniform thickness should be gradually blended from thick to thin.
5. Care must be taken that the ratio of the depth of a cored hole to its diameter does not reach a point that will result in excessive pin damage.
6. These values should be increased whenever compatible with desired design and good molding techniques.
7. Customer-Molder understanding is necessary prior to tooling.
8. These tolerances can vary greatly depending on method of molding and gate location.

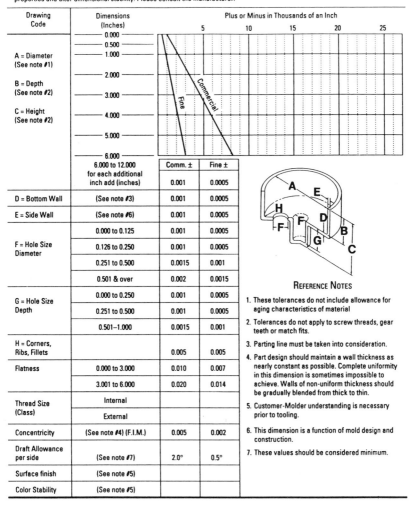

Standards & Practices of Plastics Molders		Material: Polyphenylene Ether (PPE)

Note: The *Commercial* values shown below represent common production tolerances at the most economical level. The *Fine* values represent closer tolerances that can be held but at a greater cost. Any addition of fillers will compromise physical properties and alter dimensional stability. Please consult the manufacturer.

Drawing Code	Dimensions (Inches)	Comm. ±	Fine ±
A = Diameter (See note #1)	0.000 – 6.000		
B = Depth (See note #2)			
C = Height (See note #2)			
	6.000 to 12.000 for each additional inch add (inches)	0.001	0.0005
D = Bottom Wall	(See note #3)	0.001	0.0005
E = Side Wall	(See note #6)	0.001	0.0005
F = Hole Size Diameter	0.000 to 0.125	0.001	0.0005
	0.126 to 0.250	0.001	0.0005
	0.251 to 0.500	0.0015	0.001
	0.501 & over	0.002	0.0015
G = Hole Size Depth	0.000 to 0.250	0.001	0.0005
	0.251 to 0.500	0.001	0.0005
	0.501–1.000	0.0015	0.001
H = Corners, Ribs, Fillets		0.005	0.005
Flatness	0.000 to 3.000	0.010	0.007
	3.001 to 6.000	0.020	0.014
Thread Size (Class)	Internal		
	External		
Concentricity	(See note #4) (F.I.M.)	0.005	0.002
Draft Allowance per side	(See note #7)	2.0°	0.5°
Surface finish	(See note #5)		
Color Stability	(See note #5)		

REFERENCE NOTES

1. These tolerances do not include allowance for aging characteristics of material
2. Tolerances do not apply to screw threads, gear teeth or match fits.
3. Parting line must be taken into consideration.
4. Part design should maintain a wall thickness as nearly constant as possible. Complete uniformity in this dimension is sometimes impossible to achieve. Walls of non-uniform thickness should be gradually blended from thick to thin.
5. Customer-Molder understanding is necessary prior to tooling.
6. This dimension is a function of mold design and construction.
7. These values should be considered minimum.

Reprinted from *Standards & Practices of Plastic Molders,* courtesy of The Society of the Plastics Industry, Inc.

Selected Reference Sources

- 3D Systems, Inc., Valencia, CA
- Ashland Chemical Inc., 900 Wilshire Dr., Troy, MI
- ASM International, Materials Park, OH
- Attwood Corporation, 1016 N. Monroe St., Lowell, MI
- Battenfeld of America, Inc., 31 James P. Murphy Industrial Highway, W. Warwick, RI
- Bekum Plastics Machinery, Inc., 1140 W. Grand River, Williamston, MI
- Branson Ultrasonics Corporation, Eagle Rd., Danbury, CT
- Brown Machine Company, Beaverton, MI
- Cadillac Plastic & Chemical Company, Troy, MI
- Cahners Publishing Company, *Plastics World*, 89 Franklin St., Boston, MA
- Cincinnati Milacron Company, Plastics Machinery Systems, 4165 Halfacre Rd., Batavia, OH
- Coastal Engineered Products Company, Varnville, SC
- Crane Plastics, 2141 Fairwood Ave., Columbus, OH
- DMS, 1629 Turner Rd., Windsor, Ontario, Canada
- DTM Corporation, 9921 Brecksville Rd., Brecksville, OH
- Eagle-Picher Industries, Inc., Plastic Division, 14123 Roth Rd., Grabill, IN
- Goodyear Tire & Rubber Company, 1485 Archwood Ave., Akron, OH
- Heli-Coil, Shelter Rock Lane, Danbury, CT
- Hellerbond Technology Company, 817 Phillips Rd., Columbus, OH
- Husky Injection Molding Systems Ltd., 530 Queen St. S., Bolton, Ontario, Canada
- Incoe Corporation, Troy, MI
- JARCO Rubber Products, Inc., 1010 First Ave., Jasper, IN
- Johnson Controls
- McGraw-Hill Publishing Company, *Modern Plastics Magazine*, 1221 Ave. of the Americas, New York, NY
- Meyercord Company, Carol Stream, IL

- Plastics & Computers, 164 Watchung Ave., Montclair, NJ
- Polystyrene Packaging Council, Inc., 1025 Connecticut Ave., N.W., Washington, DC
- Simco Company, Inc., 2257 N. Penn Rd., Hatfield, PA
- Society of Plastics Engineers, 14 Fairfield Dr., Brookfield, CT
- Society of the Plastics Industry, 1275 K St., N.W., Washington, DC
- Spirex Corporation, Youngstown, OH
- Steelcase, Inc., Grand Rapids, MI
- Stik-II Products, 51 Ferry St., Easthampton, MA
- TAFA Inc., 146 Pembroke Rd., Concord, NH
- Trans Tech America, Inc., Tampo, 655 W. Wise Rd., Schaumburg, IL
- Vacuum Platers Inc., 115 S. Union St., Mauston, WI

Index